Grammar and Writing 7

Workbook

First Edition

Christie Curtis

Mary Hake

Hake Publishing

Grammar and Writing 7

First Edition

Workbook

Copyright ©2011 by Hake Publishing

Printed in the United States of America

ISBN: 978-1-935839-16-3

Hake Publishing
P. O. Box 662061
Arcadia, CA 91066
www.studygrammar.com

Printing History:
5 6 7 8 9 10   15 14 13

CPSIA Tracking and Labeling Information:
Printed by Bang Printing, Brainerd, MN, USA; Job # 131567, 07/24/13

Writing 7 Contents

Introduction

The ability to communicate clearly and effectively in writing connects us with people and enhances our prospects for future success in school and in the workplace. We improve our writing skills with practice. Daily journals and informal letters, notes, or e-mails to friends and family members provide frequent opportunities to use what we have learned in our grammar and writing lessons. In addition, we must practice more formal writing exercises to prepare ourselves for writing assignments that we will receive in high school and college classes.

In *Grammar and Writing 6*, we learned to create topic sentences and to develop body paragraphs, introductory paragraphs, and concluding paragraphs in order to write different kinds of five-paragraph essays. We also wrote summaries and research papers. In *Grammar and Writing 7*, we shall write additional expository, persuasive, descriptive, and narrative essays. Then, we shall expand our writing experience to include imaginative stories, more chapter and short story summaries, longer research papers, and even some poetry.

Keeping your daily journals and your writing assignments in a **three-ring binder** will help you to organize your work so that you can easily refer back to earlier assignments when necessary.

In addition to your three-ring binder, you will need a small notebook or card file for collecting ideas, for jotting down questions or things that you notice, for saving your memories and dreams, and for writing down favorite words, names, and catchy phrases from things that you read and hear. You might even keep drawings, photos, or newspaper clippings in this notebook or file box. This is a place to keep bits and pieces that you might someday use in a story, poem, or essay. You will carry this small notebook or card file everywhere you go and make notes in it often.

Note: Lessons 1 through 31 in this Writing Packet should be completed in order. However, Lessons 32 through 35 may be introduced at any time during the school year.

Review Lesson: **The Paragraph**

The Paragraph A **paragraph** is a group of sentences that builds on a main idea, or topic. A good paragraph presents one main idea and develops it with additional sentences giving more specific information about that main idea. The supporting sentences are arranged in a logical order.

The Topic Sentence The **topic sentence** is a complete sentence telling the main idea of a paragraph. Often the topic sentence is the first sentence of a paragraph, but not always. Topic sentences are underlined in the following paragraphs:

> <u>Jasper loves the sea</u>. Every summer he camps out on the beach where he can hear the sound of the crashing waves night and day. Walking for miles along the shore, fishing from the pier, and swimming in the surf are his favorite activities.

> As Karina was brushing her teeth this morning, she noticed a small battalion of ants marching around the faucet. At lunch time she found several ants crawling around in the plastic bread bag. Further, by evening, an entire army of ants had found its way into her kitchen cupboards and were feasting on peanut butter, jelly, crackers, and cereal. <u>Karina faced a major ant invasion today</u>.

Example 1 Arrange all of the sentences below in a logical order to create one good paragraph. Then, underline the topic sentence.

- Finally, towel dry any excess drops of water from the clean window.

- Then, use the squeegee to wipe the soapy water from the window.

- To wash a window, you will need a bucket of soapy water, a scrubber, a rubber squeegee, and a towel.

- Once you have gathered your materials, you are ready to begin washing.

- First, use the scrubber to wet the window and remove dirt and grease.

We sequence the sentences to make this paragraph:

> <u>To wash a window, you will need a bucket of soapy water, a scrubber, a rubber squeegee, and a towel</u>. Once you have gathered your materials, you are ready to begin washing. First, use the scrubber to wet the window and remove dirt and grease. Then, use the squeegee to wipe the soapy water from the window. Finally, towel dry any excess drops of water from the clean window.

Paragraph.

The topic The

sentence

Example 2 Underline the topic sentence in the following paragraph:

> Every time Ms. Wright gives her English class a writing assignment, Dudley groans. Dudley hates writing. He says he cannot spell or even think of anything to write. Writing makes his brain hurt, his palms sweat, and his eyes twitch.

We see that the paragraph above is all about how Dudley hates writing. Therefore, we underline the topic sentence as follows:

> Every time Ms. Wright gives her English class a writing assignment, Dudley groans. **<u>Dudley hates writing</u>**. He says he cannot spell or even think of anything to write. Writing makes his brain hurt, his palms sweat, and his eyes twitch.

<u>Practice</u> Arrange the sentences below in a logical order to create a good paragraph. Write the paragraph on the lines provided. Then underline the topic sentence.

Answers for this Practice are found on the last page of the Writing packet.

• Just as she was ready to give up the search, Misty found Scamp sleeping peacefully behind the sofa in the living room.

• Then, she searched through the garage, the backyard, and the front yard.

• When Misty came home from school, she discovered that her cat, Scamp, was missing.

• First, she walked up and down the street, calling his name.

_____

_____

_____

_____

_____

_____

_____

_____

_____

_____

Underline the topic sentence in each paragraph below.

During math and social studies, Dudley draws cute little elves in his notebook with a pencil. Sometimes science lectures inspire him to draw exotic plants and animals. His notebook is full of intricate and interesting sketches. Dudley is an outstanding doodler!

I have never seen a bird as peculiar as the heron. A wading bird found in temperate and tropical regions, the heron has long thin legs with knobby knees. Its neck is so long and slender that I wonder how it can swallow anything. Its pointed bill and unusual head feathers give the heron an appearance unlike any other bird I have seen.

Lillian has read hundreds of stories about the wild West, and she can recite them all word for word. Lillian dreams of becoming a cowgirl someday. You will never see her wearing anything but Western attire—jeans with chaps, boots, and a bandana. Although she does not own a horse, she is saving her money to buy one.

Additional Practice Practice writing a paragraph for at least one of the following topic sentences.

1. We should choose our friends carefully.

2. Summer is an enjoyable time of the year.

3. Writing a good paragraph is an important skill.

In the next four lessons, we shall practice writing and evaluating five-paragraph essays.

LESSON 1

Parts of a Complete Essay

Our goal is to write clear, coherent, focused essays. To accomplish this, we must keep in mind the structure of a complete essay. In this lesson, we shall briefly review the **parts of a complete essay.**

Complete Essay

A **complete essay** is constructed of three main parts:

1. Introductory Paragraph

2. Body or Support Paragraphs

3. Concluding Paragraph

Now, let us recall all that is included in these three main parts of an essay.

Introductory Paragraph

The **introductory paragraph,** the first paragraph of an essay, introduces the general theme or subject of the essay. To do this, and to attract the reader's interest, the introductory paragraph contains a very clear sentence that tells exactly what the entire essay will be about. That one, very clear sentence comes near the beginning of the introductory paragraph and is called the *thesis statement.* For this reason, the introductory paragraph is often called the *thesis paragraph.*

Thesis Statement

Every essay that attempts to persuade, influence, or explain something must have a **thesis statement** in the introductory paragraph. The thesis statement not only tells the reader exactly what the essay is about but also clearly states the writer's position on the topic.

Introductory Sentence

The first sentence of an essay, the **introductory sentence,** should grab the reader's interest. This sentence can be long or short. It can be opinion or fact. It can even be more than one sentence. It is an introduction to the thesis statement, and it should make the reader want to know more about the subject of the essay.

Body Paragraphs   **Body paragraphs,** or support paragraphs, come after the first paragraph and before the final paragraph. Body paragraphs prove your point, and they provide the information that makes the reader understand exactly what you, the writer, want to communicate.

Topic Sentence   A **topic sentence** is a complete sentence, usually at the beginning of a body paragraph. It tells the reader exactly what the paragraph is about and is followed by supporting sentences.

Supporting Sentences: Experiences   **Experience sentences,** relating stories or events that you have experienced or observed, may follow a topic sentence to begin to create a full body paragraph.

Supporting Sentences: Opinions   Your opinions are your thoughts or feelings about a particular subject. **Opinion sentences,** communicating thoughts and feelings that are directly related to the topic sentence, may follow experience sentences to further develop the body paragraph.

Supporting Sentences: Facts, Examples, or Other Kinds   Some kinds of essays require more than just experience and opinion to prove a point. **Facts** or **examples** from research are sometimes necessary to support a thesis or the topic sentence of a body paragraph. Other kinds of sentences, which we shall discuss in a later lesson, include definitions, anecdotes, arguments, and analogies.

Transition   A **transition** is a word, phrase, or clause that links one subject or idea to another. A transition is placed at the beginning of a body paragraph to help the essay "flow" from one paragraph to another. Effective transitions make the ideas easier for the reader to follow. Typical transitions include the following:

Furthermore,...	*Moreover,...*
On the other hand,...	*Aside from,...*
Despite all that,...	*Instead,...*
In short,...	*Finally,...*
As a result,...	*Consequently,...*
Another thing...	*Aside from,...*
Specifically,...	*For example,...*
A final thing,...	*Generally,...*
In addition,...	*In conclusion,...*

Concluding Paragraph   The final paragraph of an essay, the **concluding paragraph,** should both summarize and reinforce the ideas and opinions expressed in the body of the essay. The concluding paragraph includes two important parts:

1. a restatement of the thesis statement
2. a reference to each of the topic sentences

Good writers know that "last words" leave a lasting impression.

Example   Here is an example of a five-paragraph essay that contains all the essential parts:

——————————————— introductory sentence

Introductory Paragraph {   We need to become skillful writers. *The ability to communicate clearly and effectively in writing connects us with people and enhances our prospects for future success in school and in the workplace.*

← thesis statement (italics)

Body Paragraphs {   In the first place, writing well allows us to communicate with other people. We can share our thoughts and feelings with others by writing personal letters, business letters, notes, and emails. Often, people's friendships and/or business relationships are dependent on their ability to keep in touch with people by way of written correspondence.

Second our success in school both now and in the future depends on our ability to write well. Teachers may require us to be able to express on paper what we have learned in classes such as social studies, English, and science. We will also need to be able to write effectively on college applications.

In addition, we shall use our writing skills in our future work place. A well-written job application might help us to acquire the job we desire. Moreover, most jobs and professions entail writing. Teachers, doctors, pastors, secretaries, mechanics, and business people all have to write daily in their workplaces.

Concluding Paragraph {   In conclusion, the ability to write skillfully will help us in our relationships with people, in our schooling, and in our future workplace. No skill is more important to our success than writing.

← restatement of thesis with reference to each topic sentence

In the essay above, transitions are circled and topic sentences are underlined.

Practice

Refer to the sample five-paragraph essay from the previous page to complete 1–5 on the blank lines provided.

1. Write the thesis statement of the essay.

_____

2. Write the introductory sentence of the essay.

_____

3. Write the topic sentence for the first body paragraph.

_____

4. Write the word group used as a transition for the first body paragraph of the essay. _____

5. Write the words used as a transition to the concluding paragraph. _____

A Memory Tool

The chart below helps us remember the essential parts of a complete, five-paragraph essay.

ESSAY PLAN

Introductory Paragraph
Introductory Sentence(s)
Thesis Statement

Body or Support Paragraph
Topic Sentence
Support Sentences:
Experience, Opinion,
Fact, Example, or Other

Body or Support Paragraph
Topic Sentence
Support Sentences:
Experience, Opinion,
Fact, Example, or Other

Body or Support Paragraph
Topic Sentence
Support Sentences:
Experience, Opinion,
Fact, Example, or Other

Concluding Paragraph
Restatement of the thesis
Reference to each topic sentence

Example   Study the chart from the previous page. Then, try to reproduce it from memory on a separate piece of paper.

We simply use this chart as a memory tool to help us keep in mind the structure of a complete essay. We may abbreviate in order to reproduce it quickly.

	Essay Plan	
Intro. Para.	Intro. Sent. Thesis Statement	
Body Para.	Top. Sent. Sup. Sents.: Exp., Op., Fact, Ex., or Other	
B. P.	T. S. S. S.: Exp., Op., Fact, Ex., or Other	
B. P.	T. S. S. S.: Exp., Op., Fact, Ex., or Other	
Concl. Para.	Restatement of thesis Ref. to each T. S.	

Practice   Study the chart showing the parts of a five-paragraph essay. Then, reproduce it from memory, abbreviating if you wish. After checking your reproduction of the chart to be sure it contains all the essential parts, place this assignment in your three-ring binder for quick reference in the future.

LESSON 2

Preparing to Write a Complete Essay

The Thesis Statement

Keeping in mind the structure of a complete essay described in Lesson 1, we will prepare to write a five-paragraph essay with the following thesis statement:

Fireworks can be dangerous.

Brainstorming

Brainstorming is a method of quickly capturing ideas about a topic or problem. One way to brainstorm is illustrated below.

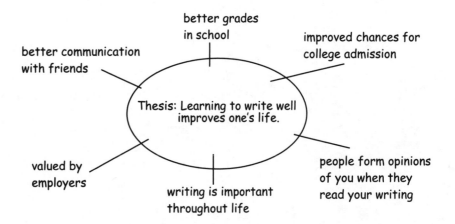

For the next few minutes, use this model to record brainstorming ideas for the thesis statement, "Fireworks can be dangerous." In the middle of a blank sheet of paper, draw a circle, three or four inches in diameter. Inside that circle, write the thesis statement. Then, quickly begin to write in the area outside the circle any and all words that come into your mind as soon as they come into your mind.

- Write quickly. Do not allow your pencil to stop moving.

- Do not worry about spelling or neatness.

- Do not worry about the word order or location.

- Do not think; just write.

Write for about three minutes, or until your paper is covered with words, whichever comes first.

When you have finished, you will almost certainly have several ideas to help you get started writing your essay.

Organizing your Ideas

After you have brainstormed, the next step is to look at the ideas you have generated and identify the ones that best support your thesis statement. Follow these steps to organize your ideas:

1. Take a moment to look at the words or groups of words that you wrote. Some of them will begin to stand out as relating very well to the thesis, and others will begin to look as though they do not belong or are not as strong.

2. Choose at least three different words or groups of words that best support the thesis. Circle them. If you cannot decide on just three, you may circle four or five. If you circle more than three words or groups of words, you have more than enough support for your thesis statement. You can write several body paragraphs of support, or you might later decide to combine one or more arguments. You might even decide to eliminate the weaker ones.

3. These circled word groups will become your body paragraph ideas. Write these ideas on a separate piece of paper leaving space underneath each idea to add more notes later for expanding the paragraphs.

4. Look at your body paragraph ideas and try to determine the order in which they should be arranged in the body of your essay to best support your thesis. Number the ideas. You can rearrange the order or even eliminate or add additional body paragraphs at any time as ideas come to you.

Forming Topic Sentences

Once you have selected the best ideas from your brainstorming and placed them on a separate page, the next step is to form those ideas into topic sentences. Each topic sentence will become a main idea for your essay's body paragraphs.

Practice

Write at least three topic sentences that clearly support your thesis statement. Keep this assignment in your three-ring binder. In Lesson 3, we shall expand these topic sentences into body paragraphs and then complete an essay.

LESSON 3

Writing a Complete Essay

In Lesson 2, you brainstormed and created ideas to support the thesis statement "Fireworks can be dangerous." You also chose the best of those ideas and put them in the order that best supports the thesis statement. Then, you used the ideas to create topic sentences. Now, you are ready to write the complete essay.

Practice Using the topic sentences that you wrote for Lesson 2, follow the steps below to complete the essay.

1. For each topic sentence, write a body paragraph to support the thesis statement. To expand your paragraph, you might add experience sentences, opinion sentences, example sentences, or fact sentences.

2. Create an introductory paragraph with an introductory sentence that will grab the reader's interest, and a sentence that states the thesis.

3. Write a concluding paragraph that includes a "clincher", a restatement of the thesis, and a reference to each of the topic sentences.

4. Add transitions between body paragraphs to make your ideas easier for the reader to follow. Pay special attention to the transition into the concluding paragraph.

5. Finally, put all the parts together to form a complete essay. As you are working, make any necessary corrections to your previous work. You might add or subtract words, or make any other change that results in a more effective essay. Keep this essay in your three-ring binder. You will evaluate it in the next lesson.

LESSON 4

Evaluating your Essay

The Writing Process

All of the writing that we do should be viewed as "work in progress." Even after you have turned in an essay to your teacher for a grade, you should not feel it can never be touched again. The knowledge that *writing is a process* should guide your thinking throughout the construction of an essay. From the first steps in organizing your thoughts, to creating body paragraphs, to adding transitions, you should feel free to make changes to improve your work.

At each step of the writing process, you should stop to re-evaluate both your thoughts and the words that you have placed on the page.

It is helpful to do this after each step of the writing process. It is also important to do this after the entire essay is written. In fact, it is probably most helpful to complete an essay, walk away from it for a day or two, and then come back and read it again.

Many times, sentences that seemed good the first time appear much different a day or two later. Furthermore, you may conceive new ideas or find clarity in ideas that were muddled. Two days later, you can write them in a way that is more meaningful to the reader.

Use the following guidelines to help you evaluate your writing.

Evaluating Your Writing

Do not be afraid to change what you have already written. Just because it was typed or written on paper in ink does not mean it cannot be improved.

Ask yourself these questions throughout the writing process:

- Is my introductory sentence interesting? *If it is not interesting to you, it certainly will not be interesting to the reader.*

- Do I have a thesis statement that clearly explains the subject of this essay? (For this assignment, the thesis was given to you.)

- Does my thesis statement clearly state my position?

- Does each body paragraph have a clear topic sentence at the beginning that tells the reader exactly what the paragraph will be about? *Read each topic sentence without the rest of the paragraph to see if it can stand alone as a strong idea.*

- Are there other personal experiences or factual examples that I can add to help improve my credibility and help the reader to better understand my point?

- In my opinion sentences, have I described my emotions and feelings so well that they create a picture in the mind of the reader to help him or her feel the same as I feel?

- Does each paragraph (except for the first) begin with an effective transition?

- Are there other arguments that I can add as additional body paragraphs to help me prove my point?

- Are some of my arguments weak and unconvincing? Should they be removed because they do not help me prove my point?

- Do my body paragraphs appear in the best possible order to prove my point? Could I place them in a different order that is more logical or effective?

- Is each sentence constructed as well as it should be? *Read each sentence in each paragraph as if it were the only sentence on the page. This helps you to catch sentence fragments, run-on sentences, misspellings, and grammatical errors.*

- Does my concluding paragraph summarize and reinforce the ideas and opinions expressed in the essay? Does it end with a "clincher" sentence?

<u>Practice</u> Use the Evaluation Form on the page following this lesson to evaluate the essay you wrote for Lesson 3. Read your essay carefully as you check for the items listed on the Evaluation Form. Write YES or NO in the blank next to each question.

When you are finished, you will either be confident that you have a strong essay, or you will know where it needs to be improved.

If you answered NO to one or more of the questions on the Evaluation Form, rewrite to improve those areas.

When you can answer YES to every question on the Evaluation Form, you will have completed this assignment.

Essay Evaluation Form

Thesis: _____

_____ Is my introductory sentence interesting? *If it is not interesting to you, it certainly will not be interesting to the reader.*

_____ Do I have a thesis statement that clearly explains the subject of this essay?

_____ Does my thesis statement clearly state my position?

_____ Does each body paragraph have a clear topic sentence at the beginning that tells the reader exactly what the paragraph will be about? *Read each topic sentence without the rest of the paragraph to see if it can stand alone as a strong idea.*

_____ Have I included personal experiences that improve my credibility and help the reader to better understand my point?

_____ In my opinion sentences, have I described my emotions and feelings so well that they create a picture in the mind of the reader to help him or her feel the same as I feel?

_____ Does each paragraph (except for the first paragraph) begin with an effective transition?

_____ Are there no other arguments that I can add as additional body paragraphs to help me prove my point?

_____ Are all of my arguments strong and convincing? Do they all help to prove my point?

_____ Do my body paragraphs appear in the best possible order to prove my point? Is their order logical and effective?

_____ Is each sentence structured as well as it could be? *Read each sentence in each paragraph as if it were the only sentence on the page. This helps you identify fragments, run-on sentences, and the overall strength or weakness of each sentence.*

_____ Does my concluding paragraph summarize and reinforce the ideas and opinions expressed in the essay? Is there a "clincher"?

LESSON 5

Different Ways of Expanding a Topic Sentence into a Paragraph

We have learned that a topic sentence states the main idea of a paragraph and that the remainder of the paragraph should clearly and completely prove that the topic sentence is true.

We have practiced developing a body paragraph by adding experience and opinion sentences to the topic sentence. In this lesson, we shall discuss other ways to develop a paragraph by adding detailed information that relates to the topic sentence. We can support a topic sentence by adding definitions, examples, facts, anecdotes, arguments, analogies, contrasts, and cause-and-effect expressions. These methods of building paragraphs will be useful when we write other types of essays in later lessons.

Notice how we use these different methods to support the following topic sentence:

> *Travelers should clearly label their baggage.*

Definitions To explain the topic sentence, we can define a term or a concept. **Definitions** may help the reader to understand more fully the meaning of the topic sentence.

> Travelers should clearly label their baggage. *To label is to affix a gummed piece of paper, or tag, to an article in order to identify its contents or owner.*

Examples An **example** is a sample or an illustration. In almost any kind of writing, examples help to clarify a topic sentence. They offer the reader evidence.

> Travelers should clearly label their baggage. *For example, using bright pink ribbon, my aunt ties a large name tag to her suitcase. This way, she can easily recognize her own bag.*

Facts A **fact** is a piece of information that can be proved to be true. It is a *fact*, for example, that Alaska is the largest state in the Union. An *opinion*, on the other hand, is a judgment or belief. That Alaska is the most beautiful state in the Union is an *opinion*. It cannot be proved. Below, we add a fact to support the topic sentence.

> Travelers should clearly label their baggage. *The Fourth-Street Bus Station loses an average of six pieces of unmarked luggage every week day.*

Anecdotes To entertain the reader while illustrating our point, we can write an **anecdote,** a short account of an incident, something that happened to us or to someone we know, which relates to the topic sentence.

> Travelers should clearly label their baggage. *As I began to unpack after my trip to Peru, I was shocked to find a suitcase full of diapers and baby clothes! Obviously, I had brought home someone else's bag and not my own.*

Arguments In some kinds of writing, especially in persuasive writing, logical **arguments** can help to support our topic sentence. An argument might seek to disprove an opposing viewpoint.

> Travelers should clearly label their baggage. *Some people think this is unnecessary, but it only takes a minute, and it can save travelers the frustration of losing their valuable possessions.*

Analogies Sometimes we can use an **analogy** to clarify a point. An analogy is a comparison. To be effective, the two things being compared must have many similarities. Usually interesting to a reader, an analogy will help the reader to better understand the topic sentence.

> Travelers should clearly label their baggage. *Without a name tag, a suitcase in the baggage claim area may be as difficult to find as a needle in a haystack.*

Contrast Sometimes **contrast** helps to highlight our claim.

> Travelers should clearly label their baggage. *Most people carefully check identification tags when they claim their luggage, but others are careless and grab the first bag that looks like theirs.*

Cause and Effect Sentences showing **cause and effect** can clarify our meaning.

> Travelers should clearly label their baggage. *Many suitaces and bags are alike in shape, size, and*

19

color. This can cause confusion at the baggage claim area of an airport.

Practice For a–f, use this topic sentence: *We need to clean our desks to prevent the accumulation of too much clutter.*

a. Write a *definition* that could be used to expand the topic sentence above.

b. Write an *example* that might follow the topic sentence above.

c. Write a *fact* to support the topic sentence.

d. Write an *anecdote* to illustrate the topic sentence.

e. Write an *argument* that might prove the topic sentence.

f. Write an *analogy*, or comparison, to clarify the topic sentence.

Additional Practice Using the methods that you have learned in this lesson, expand each of the following topic sentences into a paragraph of at least five sentences.

1. Everyone can benefit from some kind of physical exercise.

2. Learning to save and budget money is an important step in becoming an adult.

3. A balanced diet is necessary for good health.

4. Sometimes advertisements deceive people.

5. Laughter is good medicine.

LESSON
6

Preparing to Write a Persuasive (Argument) Essay

Four Purposes for Writing

Every piece of writing has a purpose. There are four basic purposes for writing: narrative, expository, descriptive, and persuasive.

Narrative writing tells a story or relates a series of events. A letter describing your five-day backpack trip in the High Sierras would be narrative writing. In Lesson 19, you will write a narrative essay telling about a personal experience of your choice.

Expository writing gives information or explains. A scientific article entitled "How a Microwave Works" is an example of expository writing. Your essay explaining that fireworks can be dangerous was also an example of expository writing.

Descriptive writing describes a person, place, or thing. Examples include a brochure describing beautiful Glacier Bay in Alaska, a personal composition about your favorite cousin, and a "Lost Dog" poster that tells exactly what the lost dog looks like. In Lesson 22, you will practice this type of writing by describing a person whom you can observe.

Persuasive writing attempts to convince someone to do or believe something. An advertisement for Tuff Cotton Balls, an article about the importance of saving an old oak tree from being uprooted by housing developers, and a campaign flyer urging voters to elect a certain candidate are all examples of persuasive writing.

The Persuasive (Argument) Essay

Keeping in mind the structure of a complete essay described in Lesson 1, we shall prepare to write a persuasive (argument) essay using the following sentence as our thesis statement:

People should not be allowed to smoke in restaurants.

The goal of this essay will be to convince or *persuade* the reader that people should not be allowed to smoke in restaurants.

Persuasive essays usually deal with controversial topics, subjects that have two sides, or opinions. If you prefer, you

may argue the opposite side and rewrite the thesis statement to read, "People *should* be allowed to smoke in restaurants."

Your essay will prove that your thesis statement is correct. You will convince the reader of this, maintaining a formal style. We avoid using first person pronouns (I, we, me, my, our) in formal writing.

Acknowledging opposing claims will strengthen your arguments:

> Some people claim that…(opposing claim), but facts prove that…(your thesis).

> One may argue that…(opposing claim). However, research shows that…(your thesis) is true.

Brainstorming Brainstorming is always our first step in writing an essay. Recall from Writing Lesson 2 that we draw a circle in the middle of a blank sheet of paper. Inside the circle, write the thesis statement. Then, quickly begin to write in the area outside the circle any and all words that come into your mind as soon as they come into your mind.

- Write quickly, and do not worry about spelling or neatness.

- Write for about three minutes or until your paper is covered with words, whichever comes first.

Organizing your Ideas After you have brainstormed, look at the ideas that you have generated and identify the ones that best support your thesis statement. Follow these steps to organize your ideas:

1. Take a moment to look at the words or groups of words that you wrote. Some of them will begin to stand out as relating very well to the thesis; they will firmly argue your point and convince the reader. Others will begin to look as though they do not belong or are not as strong.

2. Choose at least three different words or groups of words that best support the thesis. Circle them. If you cannot decide on just three, you may circle four or five. If you circle more than three words or groups of words, you have more than enough support for your thesis statement. You can write several body paragraphs of support, or you might later decide to combine one or more arguments. You might even decide to eliminate the weaker ones.

3. These circled word groups will become your body paragraph ideas. Write these ideas on a separate piece of paper, leaving space underneath each idea to add more notes later for expanding the paragraphs.

4. Look at your body paragraph ideas and try to determine the order in which they should be arranged in the body of your essay to best support your thesis. Number the ideas. You can rearrange the order or even eliminate or add additional body paragraphs at any time as ideas come to you.

Forming Topic Sentences Once you have selected the best ideas from your brainstorming and placed them on a separate page, take those ideas and form them into topic sentences. Each topic sentence will become a main idea for your essay's body paragraphs.

Practice Write at least three topic sentences that clearly support your thesis statement. Keep this assignment in your three-ring binder. In Lesson 7, we shall develop these topic sentences into body paragraphs and then complete the persuasive essay.

LESSON 7

Writing the Persuasive (Argument) Essay

In Lesson 6, you prepared to write your persuasive (argument) essay. By brainstorming, you gathered ideas. You chose the best of those ideas and put them in the order that best supports your thesis statement. Then, you used the ideas to create at least three topic sentences. Now you are ready to write the complete essay.

Practice Using the topic sentences you wrote for Lesson 6, follow the steps below to complete the persuasive essay.

1. For each topic sentence, write a body paragraph to support the thesis statement. Refer back to Lesson 5 for different ways to expand a topic sentence into a paragraph. In addition to experience and opinion sentences, you might write definitions, examples, facts, anecdotes, arguments, analogies, and other relevant evidence to support the topic sentence. Keep in mind that acknowledging alternate or opposing claims will make your arguments stronger.

2. Create an introductory paragraph and a concluding paragraph. Remember that the introductory sentence should grab the reader's interest and that the "last words" of your conclusion will leave a lasting impression.

3. Add transitions between body paragraphs to make your ideas easier for the reader to follow. Pay special attention to the transition into the concluding paragraph. Refer to transitions in Lesson 1.

4. Finally, put all the parts together to form a complete essay. As you are working, make any necessary corrections to your previous work. You might add things, take things out, or make any other change that results in a more convincing, persuasive essay.

Additional Practice (Optional) After you have evaluated your persuasive essay using the guidelines in Lesson 8, you might try writing another persuasive essay on one of these topics, choosing "should" or "should not" to complete your thesis statement:

1. Our school day (should, should not) be shortened by one hour.

24

2. The federal government (should, should not) spend more money funding research for the cure of cancer.

3. California home owners (should, should not) be allowed to remove healthy oak trees from their property.

4. Mountain lions (should, should not) be allowed to roam free in areas where people live.

5. People (should, should not) have to pay a fee to camp in the National Forest.

6. High-school students (should, should not) be allowed to wear whatever they want to school.

7. Fourteen-year-olds (should, should not) be allowed to drive.

LESSON 8

Evaluating the Persuasive (Argument) Essay

We have learned that all of the writing we do is "work in progress." The knowledge that *writing is a process* guides our thinking throughout the construction of an essay. From the first steps in organizing our thoughts, to creating body paragraphs, to adding transitions, we constantly make changes to improve our work.

At each step of the writing process, we should stop to re-evaluate both our thoughts and the words that we have placed on the page.

Evaluating Your Writing

In Lesson 7, you completed your persuasive essay. Now that some time has passed, you are ready to evaluate it using the following guidelines.

Ask yourself these questions:

- Is my introductory sentence interesting? *If it is not interesting to you, it certainly will not be interesting to the reader.*

- Does my thesis statement clearly state my position?

- Have I acknowledged opposing arguments?

- Does each body paragraph have a clear topic sentence at the beginning that tells the reader exactly what the paragraph will be about? *Read each topic sentence without the rest of the paragraph to see if it can stand alone as a strong idea.*

- Does each of my topic sentences strongly support my thesis statement?

- Are there other personal experiences, facts, examples, arguments, anecdotes, or analogies, that I can add to help improve my credibility and help the reader to better understand my point?

- Have I described in my opinion sentences my emotions and feeling so well that they create a picture in the mind of the reader to help him or her feel the same as I feel?

- Does each paragraph (except for the first) begin with an effective, relational transition?

- Are there other arguments that I can add as additional body paragraphs to help me prove my point?

- Are some of my arguments weak and unconvincing? Should they be removed because they do not help me prove my point?

- Do my body paragraphs appear in the best possible order to prove my point? Could I place them in a different order that is more logical or effective?

- Is each sentence constructed as well as it should be? *Read each sentence in each paragraph as if it were the only sentence on the page. This helps you to catch sentence fragments, run-on sentences, misspellings, and grammatical errors.*

- Does my concluding paragraph summarize and reinforce the ideas and opinions expressed in the essay? Have I convinced the reader that my thesis statement is true?

Practice Use the Evaluation Form on the page following this lesson to evaluate the persuasive essay you wrote for Lesson 7. Read your essay carefully as you check for the items listed on the Evaluation Form. Write YES or NO in the blank next to each question.

When you are finished, you will either be confident that you have a strong essay, or you will know where it needs to be improved.

If you answered NO to one or more of the questions on the Evaluation Form, rewrite to improve those areas.

When you can answer YES to every question on the Evaluation Form, you will have completed this assignment.

27

Persuasive Essay Evaluation Form

Thesis: _____

_____ Is my introductory sentence interesting? *If it is not interesting to you, it certainly will not be interesting to the reader.*

_____ Do I have a thesis statement that clearly explains the subject of this essay?

_____ Does my thesis statement clearly state my position?

_____ Does each body paragraph have a clear topic sentence at the beginning that tells the reader exactly what the paragraph will be about? *Read each topic sentence without the rest of the paragraph to see if it can stand alone as a strong idea.*

_____ Are there no other experiences, facts, or examples that I can add to help improve my credibility and help the reader to better understand my point?

_____ In my opinion sentences, have I described my emotions and feelings so well that they create a picture in the mind of the reader to help him or her feel the same as I feel?

_____ Does each paragraph (except for the first paragraph) begin with an effective transition?

_____ Are there no other arguments that I can add as additional body paragraphs to help me prove my point?

_____ Are all of my arguments strong and convincing? Have I acknowledge opposing arguments?

_____ Do my body paragraphs appear in the best possible order to prove my point?

_____ Is each sentence structured as well as it could be? *Read each sentence in each paragraph as if it were the only sentence on the page. This helps you identify fragments, run-on sentences, and the overall strength or weakness of each sentence.*

_____ Does my concluding paragraph summarize and reinforce the ideas and opinions expressed in the essay? Is there a strong "clincher" sentence?

28

LESSON 9

Writing a Strong Thesis Statement

The thesis statement clearly tells what the entire essay is about. We have practiced writing a complete essay based on an assigned thesis statement. In this lesson, we shall practice creating our own thesis statements for assigned topics.

We remember that the thesis statement not only tells the reader exactly what the essay is about but also clearly states the writer's position on the topic.

Brainstorming When faced with an assigned topic, we prepare by brainstorming in order to generate ideas and thoughts.

The first step in brainstorming is choosing your direction. You would not get into a car and just begin to drive, expecting to arrive at nowhere in particular. You need to know where you are going before you pull out of the driveway. In other words, you must think about the topic, choose your direction or focus, and prepare to define what your essay is about.

For example, if the assignment is to write about the qualities that make a good friend, your thesis statement could begin, "The qualities that make a good friend are ..."

After brainstorming about the topic, perhaps you have decided that there are four specific qualities that make a good friend. If so, your thesis statement might be the following:

There are four important qualities that make a good friend.

Practice Below are ten topics that could be given to you as subjects for essays. For each topic, brainstorm briefly. Then, write a declarative sentence that could be used as a strong thesis statement for a complete essay.

1. The best things about vacations from school

2. The things you like best about school

3. Why a person should learn a foreign language

4. Things that you would like to change about yourself

29

5. What you will do differently as a student this year from what you did last year

6. Some ways that you can help to make the world a better place

7. Some events that you will always remember

8. What you can do to improve or maintain your physical health

9. Some skills you would like to acquire

10. Kinds of things that make you happy

LESSON 10

Preparing to Write an Expository (Informative) Essay

The purpose of expository writing is to inform or explain. Expository writing tells why or how. The following might be titles for expository essays:

"How to Grow Delicious Turnips"

"New Burglar Alarm Technology"

"Where to Shop for Antiques"

"Why the Tortoise Makes a Good Pet"

"Building a Bird House from Scrap Lumber"

A good expository essay is well organized and clear. It might offer an explanation of how something works, information about a specific subject, or instructions for doing something. It is objective and formal in style and tone, using precise language.

In this lesson, we shall prepare to write an expository essay that explains how to wash a car.

Our goal is to write easy-to-follow instructions, which will require a detailed description of the process. Therefore, we shall break down the actions and carefully sequence them in a logical or practical order so that the reader can understand our step-by-step method of washing a car inside and out.

Brainstorming To generate thoughts and ideas, we shall brainstorm before creating a thesis statement for our *how-to* essay.

- Write quickly, and do not worry about spelling or neatness.

- Write for about three minutes or until your paper is covered with words, whichever comes first.

Writing a Thesis Statement Now, it is time to state the purpose of your essay in a clear thesis statement. Using the ideas you have written by brainstorming, write a sentence that tells what your essay is about. Hint: Will you be presenting a certain number of *steps* in your how-to essay? Or, will you be explaining a number of different *ways* to wash a car? Your thesis statement will reveal your presentation plan.

31

Organizing your Ideas

After you have written a strong thesis statement telling what your essay is about, look at the ideas you have generated by brainstorming and identify the ones that best support your thesis statement. When writing an expository essay, it is sometimes helpful to make an outline to help you organize your ideas. For example, your outline might look something like this:

How to Wash a Car

I. Preparation
    A. Appropriate dress
        1. Old clothes
        2. Shoes that water won't ruin
    B. Materials
        1. Bucket of soapy water
        2. Hose
        3. Towels

II. Process
    A. Cleaning inside of car
        1. Vacuuming
        2. Washing windows
        3. Deodorizing
    B. Cleaning outside of car
        1. Soaping
        2. Scrubbing
        3. Rinsing
        4. Drying
    C. Cleaning special parts of car
        1. Tires
        2. Mirrors and windows
        3. Chrome

III. Afterward
    A. Clean-up of towels, buckets, hose, etc.
    B. How the car should look and smell

For this assignment, you may either use the outline above, or you may create your own outline or thought clusters based on the ideas that you generated while brainstorming. If you choose to use an outline, each Roman numeral part of your

outline will represent a body paragraph to be developed later. You should have at least three of these.

Tone The **tone** of an essay reflects the writer's attitude toward the topic. Tone can be formal or informal, sarcastic or straight-forward, serious or silly, admiring or critical. Before you begin writing, you must decide on your tone. The expository essay is formal and objective in tone and style, presenting facts rather than opinions and avoiding the use of first person pronouns (I, me, my, we, us, our).

Forming Topic Sentences Once you have decided on your tone, selected the main ideas from your brainstorming, and arranged them in clusters or an outline, take those ideas and form them into topic sentences. Each topic sentence will become a main idea for your essay's body paragraphs. These sentences may include relevant facts, concrete details, quotations, and examples.

Practice Write a thesis statement and at least three topic sentences that clearly explain your thesis statement. Keep this assignment in your three-ring binder. In Lesson 11, we shall develop these topic sentences into body paragraphs and then complete the expository essay.

33

LESSON 11

Writing the Expository (Informative) Essay

In Lesson 10, you prepared to write your expository essay about how to wash a car. By brainstorming, you gathered ideas and wrote a thesis statement. You chose the best of those ideas and put them into clusters or an outline to create a logical order, or organization, for your presentation. Then, you used the main ideas to create at least three topic sentences. Now, you are ready to write the complete essay.

Practice   Using the topic sentences you wrote for Lesson 10, follow the steps below to complete the expository essay.

1. For each topic sentence, write a body paragraph to support the thesis statement. Refer to your notes or outline, and use the ideas underneath each Roman numeral to write body sentences that further explain, or expand, each topic sentence.

2. Create an introductory paragraph and a concluding paragraph. Remember that the introductory sentence should grab the reader's interest and that the "last words" of your conclusion will leave a lasting impression.

3. Add transitions between body paragraphs to make your ideas easier for the reader to follow. Transitions that indicate order, such as "the first step..." or "the second step...," are appropriate in a how-to essay. Pay special attention to the transition into the concluding paragraph. Use appropriate links to join connected ideas within your essay.

4. Finally, put all the parts together to form a complete essay. As you are working, make any necessary corrections to your previous work. You might add things, take things out, or make any other change that results in a clearer, easier-to-follow expository essay. Consider using multimedia, illustrations, or graphics, such as charts and tables, if these will help the reader's understanding.

Additional Practice   (Optional) After you have evaluated your expository essay using the guidelines in Lesson 12, you might try writing another expository essay on a topic of your choice or on one of these topics:

34

1. Explain how to play a game, any game with which you are familiar.

2. Write an essay giving at least three reasons why your school is the best in the country.

3. Introduce your reader to an interesting person, such as one of your relatives, family members, or friends.

4. Write an essay about the proper care and feeding of an animal with which you are familiar.

5. Read about cowbirds and then write an essay explaining how they are different from other small birds.

6. Compare and contrast the alligator and the crocodile.

35

LESSON 12

Evaluating the Expository (Informative) Essay

We remember that all of our writing is "work in progress." The knowledge that *writing is a process* guides our thinking throughout the construction of an essay. Throughout the steps of brainstorming, organizing our thoughts, creating body paragraphs, and adding transitions, we constantly make changes to improve our work.

Evaluating Your Writing

In Lesson 11, you completed your expository essay. Now that some time has passed, you are ready to evaluate it using the following guidelines.

Ask yourself these questions:

- Is my introductory sentence interesting? *If it is not interesting to you, it certainly will not be interesting to the reader.*

- Does my thesis statement clearly state what my essay is about?

- Does each body paragraph have a clear topic sentence at the beginning that tells the reader exactly what the paragraph will be about? *Read each topic sentence without the rest of the paragraph to see if it can stand alone as a strong idea.*

- Does each of my topic sentences strongly support my thesis statement?

- Are there other details, facts, examples, quotations, or steps, that I can add to help improve my explanation or help the reader to better follow my instructions?

- Have I provided complete definitions of my terms?

- Do I need to provide comparison or contrasting statements?

- Are cause and effect statements needed?

- Are my sentences in a logical or practical order?

- Does each paragraph (except for the first) begin with an effective transition?

- Are there other details that I can add as additional body paragraphs to create a fuller or clearer explanation?

- Are some of my sentences weak or confusing? Should they be removed because they do not help me to explain?

- Do my body paragraphs appear in the best possible order? Could I place them in a different order that is more logical or effective?

- Is each sentence constructed as well as it should be? *Read each sentence in each paragraph as if it were the only sentence on the page. This helps you to catch sentence fragments, run-on sentences, misspellings, and grammatical errors.*

- Does my concluding paragraph summarize and reinforce the ideas expressed in the essay? Is there a "clincher" sentence?

Practice   Use the Evaluation Form on the page following this lesson to evaluate the expository essay that you wrote for Lesson 11. Read your essay carefully as you check for the items listed on the Evaluation Form. Write YES or NO in the blank next to each question.

When you are finished, you will either be confident that you have a strong essay, or you will know where it needs to be improved.

If you answered NO to one or more of the questions on the Evaluation Form, rewrite to improve those areas.

When you can answer YES to every question on the Evaluation Form, you will have completed this assignment.

37

Expository Essay Evaluation Form

Thesis: _____

_____ Is my introductory sentence interesting? *If it is not interesting to you, it certainly will not be interesting to the reader.*

_____ Do I have a thesis statement that clearly explains the subject of this essay?

_____ Does my thesis statement clearly state my method of presentation?

_____ Does each body paragraph have a clear topic sentence at the beginning that tells the reader exactly what the paragraph will be about? *Read each topic sentence without the rest of the paragraph to see if it can stand alone as a strong idea.*

_____ Have I defined technical terms and included every concrete detail, relevant fact, quotation, or example that I can to help improve my explanation and help the reader to better understand my point?

_____ Within each paragraph, are my sentences in a logical or practical order?

_____ Does each paragraph (except for the first paragraph) begin with an effective transition?

_____ Are there no other ideas that I can add as additional body paragraphs to create a fuller or clearer explanation?

_____ Are all of my sentences strong and clear? Do they all help me to explain?

_____ Do my body paragraphs appear in the best possible order? Is their order logical and effective?

_____ Is each sentence structured as well as it could be? *Read each sentence in each paragraph as if it were the only sentence on the page. This helps you identify fragments, run-on sentences, and the overall strength or weakness of each sentence.*

_____ Does my concluding paragraph summarize and reinforce the ideas expressed in the essay? Is there a "clincher" sentence?

38

LESSON 13

Developing an Outline

We have learned that an outline can help us to organize our ideas for an expository essay. In an outline, we can arrange and sequence thoughts in a logical manner.

In this lesson, we shall review the basic outline form and practice developing an outline from an essay that we have already written. This exercise will give us confidence in our ability to make an outline in preparation for writing future essays or research papers.

Outline Form

An **outline** is a list of topics and subtopics arranged in an organized form. We use Roman numerals for main topics. For subtopics, we use uppercase letters. For a very detailed outline, we use alternating numbers and letters as shown below.

Title

I. Main topic

  A. Subtopic of I

  B. Subtopic of I

    1. Subtopic of B

    2. Subtopic of B

      a. Subtopic of 2

      b. Subtopic of 2

        (1) Subtopic of b

        (2) Subtopic of b

          (a) Subtopic of (2)

          (b) Subtopic of (2)

II. Main topic

  A. Etc.

    1. Etc.

Notice that we indent subtopics so that all letters or numbers of the same kind will come directly under one another in a vertical line. Notice also that we use **at least two subdivisions** (letters or numbers of the same kind) for a category.

39

Topic Outline An outline may be either a topic outline or a sentence outline. In a **topic outline,** each main topic or subtopic is written as a single word or phrase. Below is an example of a topic outline of the first part of an essay on objections to homework.

Homework Hassles

I. Why homework is necessary
   A. To learn new things
   B. To practice skills

II. Why some homework is irritating
   A. Too repetitious
   B. Too time-consuming

Sentence Outline In a **sentence outline,** each topic is expressed as a complete sentence. Notice how the sentence outline below communicates more meaning than the short phrases of the topic outline.

Homework Hassles

I. Homework is necessary.
   A. We learn new things as we do our homework.
   B. Homework provides practice that increases skills.

II. Some homework is irritating.
   A. Too much repetition is irritating.
   B. Homework that consumes much time is irritating.

Practice On a separate sheet of paper, practice the outlining process by organizing the following set of information in a topic outline form. First, look carefully over the list. You will find *one* main topic (I.) and *three* subtopics (A., B., and C.). The rest of the items will be sub-subtopics, or subtopics of subtopics (1., 2., 3.,...). You might begin by circling the main topic and underlining the three subtopics. You may work with your teacher or with a group of students for this project.

The completed outline (answer) for this Practice is found on the last page of the Writing packet.

exclamation mark	period
subject	noun
grammatical terms	parts of speech
comma	semicolon
pronoun	parts of a sentence
predicate	adjective

Topic Outline

preposition   direct object

colon   dash

punctuation marks   verb

adverb   question mark

interjection   conjunction

quotation marks   indirect object

Additional Practice For Lesson 3, you wrote a complete essay containing at least three body paragraphs. Create a topic outline covering the body paragraphs of that essay. Hint: The topic sentence of each body paragraph will become a word or phrase beside a Roman numeral indicating a main topic in your outline. Therefore, your outline will have at least three Roman numerals.

Additional Practice (Optional) For Lesson 7, you wrote a persuasive essay containing at least three body paragraphs. Create a topic outline for this essay.

41

LESSON 14

Preparing to Write a Research Paper: The Working Bibliography

A research paper is a type of expository writing based on information gathered from a variety of reliable sources. In the future, you may be asked to write a research paper for an English, history, science, art, or music class. Knowing the procedure for writing a good research paper will help you to become a successful high school and college student.

In this lesson, we shall learn how to prepare for writing a research paper on an assigned subject. To practice the procedure, you may choose one of the following subjects:

1. The Opossum, a Good Neighbor

2. How the Internet Got Started

3. Isaac Newton's Contribution to Our Understanding of Color

4. How to Avoid Botulism When Canning Pickles

5. A subject suggested by your teacher

Tone The research paper requires a serious tone. The writing should be formal and impersonal. Therefore, we do not use first person pronouns, such as *I, me,* or *my.*

Gathering Sources of Information The first step in researching your subject is to compile a **working bibliography,** a collection of possible sources of information. Consider the following possibilities for your research:

• library research aids including card catalog, *Readers' Guide*, and reference works

• Internet

• government publications

• personal interviews or correspondence

• museums

• scholarly journals

• Google Scholar

42

Evaluating Sources of Information

Not all sources are reliable or useful. We must evaluate each source for its usefulness. Asking the following questions will help us to evaluate each source:

1. *Is the information current?* A 1970 study of smog in large cities is out-of-date. Therefore, it would not be an appropriate source for a paper on today's pollution problems except for drawing comparisons with the past.

2. *Is the source objective and impartial?* An article written by the president of Mountain Spring Bottled Water about impurities in local well water might not be an objective source. The author could be trying to sell you something.

3. *For what audience was the source intended?* Material written for young children might be over-simplified while material written for specialists might be too technical.

Preparing Bibliography Cards

After gathering sources, evaluating each one for its usefulness, and choosing only those that are appropriate, we are ready to compile a working bibliography, the list of sources from which we will glean information for our research paper. Using three-by-five inch index cards, we record each source on a separate card. We include all the information listed below, for we will need it to prepare our final bibliography when our paper is completed.

BOOKS

1. Author's (or editor's) full name, last name first. Indicate editor by placing *ed.* after the name. If the book has more than one author, only the first author is written last name first. Others are written first name first.

2. Title and subtitle underlined

3. City of publication

4. Publisher's name

5. Most recent copyright year

MAGAZINE, NEWSPAPER, JOURNAL, AND ENCYCLOPEDIA ARTICLES

1. Author's (or editor's) full name, last name first. Indicate editor by placing *ed.* after the name. If the article has more than one author, only the first author is written last name first. Others are written first name first.

43

2. Title of article in quotation marks

3. Name of magazine, newspaper, journal, or encyclopedia underlined

4. Date and page numbers of *magazines*
   Date, edition, section, page numbers of *newspapers*
   Volume, year, page numbers of *journals*
   Edition and year of *encyclopedias*

ELECTRONIC SOURCES

1. Author's (or editor's) full name, last name first. Indicate editor by placing *ed.* after the name. If the article has more than one author, only the first author is written last name first. Others are written first name first.

2. Title of article in quotation marks

3. Books, magazines, newspapers, journals, encyclopedias, or Web sites underlined

4. Date and page numbers of magazines

   Date, edition, section, page numbers of newspapers.

   Volume, year, page numbers of journals

   Edition and year of encyclopedia

   City of publication, publisher's name, and most recent copyright year of books

5. The date that you accessed the source

6. The URL in angle brackets

44

We assign each bibliography card a "source number" and write it in the upper left corner. Later we will use this number to identify the sources of our notes. Below are some sample bibliography cards.

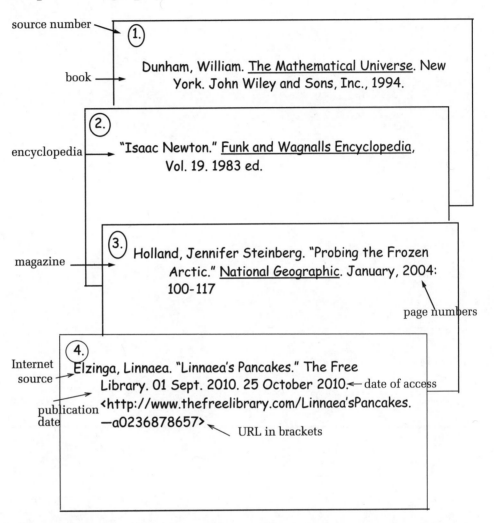

source number

1.

book → Dunham, William. <u>The Mathematical Universe</u>. New York. John Wiley and Sons, Inc., 1994.

2.

encyclopedia → "Isaac Newton." <u>Funk and Wagnalls Encyclopedia</u>, Vol. 19. 1983 ed.

3.

magazine → Holland, Jennifer Steinberg. "Probing the Frozen Arctic." <u>National Geographic</u>. January, 2004: 100-117

page numbers

4.

Internet source → Elzinga, Linnaea. "Linnaea's Pancakes." The Free Library. 01 Sept. 2010. 25 October 2010. ← date of access

publication date → <http://www.thefreelibrary.com/Linnaea'sPancakes. —a0236878657> ← URL in brackets

Practice After you have chosen a subject from the list of suggestions for your research paper, follow the instructions in this lesson for gathering and evaluating sources and for preparing bibliography cards. Locate at least *four* appropriate sources and prepare a bibliography card for each one. Remember to assign each card a source number and write it in the upper left corner.

45

LESSON 15

Preparing to Write a Research Paper: Notes, Thesis, Outline

In Lesson 14, you chose a subject for a research paper and created a working bibliography, four or more sources of information that you will use for your paper. In this lesson, you will take notes from these sources, organize your notes, create a thesis statement, and develop an outline for your paper.

Taking Notes It is helpful to use four-by-six inch index cards for taking notes. As you read through your sources, write down information that applies to your subject. Write most of your notes in your own words. You may summarize the author's main ideas, or you may record specific facts or details in your own words. If you quote the author, you must enclose the author's exact words in quotation marks.

Whenever you take notes from a source, you must credit that source whether you quote an author or use your own words. Do not *plagiarize*, or use another person's words or ideas, without acknowledging the source.

In the upper right corner of your note card, you will enter the source number from your working bibliography.

At the end of each note, write the page or pages on which you found the information.

Below is a sample note card.

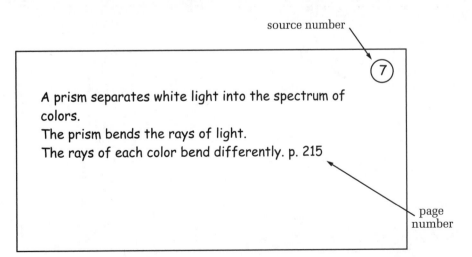

source number

⑦

A prism separates white light into the spectrum of colors.
The prism bends the rays of light.
The rays of each color bend differently. p. 215

page
number

46

Organizing Your Information After you have taken notes on all your sources and gathered sufficient information for your research paper, take some time to organize your note cards and arrange them in a logical order.

Thesis Statement Now look over your organized notes, and write a thesis statement that clearly explains the main idea of your research paper.

Outline In Lesson 13, you learned to develop an outline. Use your organized note cards to help you create an informal topic outline for your research paper. This outline will guide you as you begin to write the first draft of your paper in the next lesson.

Practice Follow the instructions in this lesson for taking notes from your sources. Then, organize your notes, write a thesis statement, and develop an outline for your research paper.

47

LESSON 16

Writing the Research Paper

In Lesson 15, you took notes from your sources, organized your notes, wrote a thesis statement, and created an outline for your research paper.

Writing the First Draft

With your outline, your thesis statement, your notes, and your bibliography cards in front of you, you are ready to begin writing the first draft of your research paper. A first draft is a rough copy that is for your use only. It is meant to be revised again and again until you are satisfied with it.

As you write, keep in mind your thesis statement, your purpose, and the need for a formal tone. Use the information on your note cards to support your thesis and to fill in the details as you follow your outline for organization.

Create an introductory paragraph that captures the reader's attention. Consider beginning with an interesting statement, an anecdote, or an example. Make certain that your opening paragraph includes your thesis statement.

Use the main points in your outline to create topic sentences for your body paragraphs. Then, develop these topic sentences into paragraphs, making sure that all of your information relates to your thesis statement.

Pay special attention to transitions as you begin each new paragraph.

Your concluding paragraph will summarize and reinforce the ideas set forth in the rest of your research paper.

Documentation of Sources

Writing the first draft of a research paper involves bringing together information from your different sources, which you must acknowledge properly. We call this acknowledgement the **documentation** of sources.

As you write, you must credit your sources for both ideas and quotations. There are various methods of documenting sources for research papers. In this book, we shall practice a method called *parenthetical citations*. This form identifies sources in parentheses that are placed as close as possible to the ideas or quotations that we are citing. Inside the parentheses, we place a reference to the source in our bibliography, which is found at the end of the research paper.

48

Usually, the reference inside the parentheses consists only of an author's last name and the page number from which the material was taken. For example, (McKeever 42) would appear right after an idea taken from page forty-two in John McKeever's book, which is listed in the bibliography.

When no author and only a title is given for a source, we place a shortened form of the title and the page number or numbers in the parentheses: ("Black Holes" 215-217).

Notice that the end punctuation for a sentence containing borrowed material is placed *after* the parenthetical citation:

> The pulling power of black holes is so strong that even light cannot escape from them (McKeever 42).
>
> punctuation mark

The highly respected Modern Language Association (MLA) gives us many more detailed guidelines for parenthetical citations. However, in this lesson we shall follow the simplified instructions above.

The Bibliography

The bibliography, the list of the sources that you used as you wrote your paper, comes at the end of the research paper.

Follow these steps to create your bibliography:

1. Alphabetize your bibliography cards according to the last names of the authors or the first important word in a title if there is no author.

2. Copy the information from all of your alphabetized bibliography cards under the title "Bibliography" or "Works Cited."

3. Indent all lines after the first line of each entry and punctuate as shown in the example below.

Bibliography

Grim, Edmund. "Six Ways to Clean the Sewer." Home and Grounds Journal July 1999: 12-15.

Leadfoot, Doris. A Study in Dynamics. New York, Grassvale Publishers, 2001.

In high school and college, you will learn to follow more detailed guidelines given by MLA for bibliographic entries. However, in this lesson you may follow the simplified

instructions above unless your teacher advises you to do otherwise.

Practice Follow the procedure given in this lesson for writing the first draft of your research paper, documenting your sources, and making your bibliography.

50

LESSON 17

Evaluating the Research Paper

The knowledge that *writing is a process* guides our thinking throughout the construction of our research paper. From the first steps in choosing our subject, to gathering information and organizing our thoughts, to creating body paragraphs, to adding transitions, we constantly make changes to improve our work.

Evaluating Your Writing

In Lesson 16, you completed the first draft of your research paper. Now that some time has passed, you are ready to evaluate it using the following guidelines.

Ask yourself these questions:

- Are my sources reliable, objective, and current?

- Is my introductory sentence interesting? *If it is not interesting to you, it certainly will not be interesting to the reader.*

- Does my thesis clearly state the purpose of my paper?

- Does the beginning of the research paper clearly establish a formal, serious tone?

- Does each body paragraph have a clear topic sentence at the beginning that tells the reader exactly what the paragraph will be about? *Read each topic sentence without the rest of the paragraph to see if it can stand alone as a strong idea.*

- Does each paragraph include specific details and examples from my research?

- Have I correctly documented each piece of borrowed information?

- Are my sentences in a logical order?

- Does each paragraph (except for the first) begin with an effective transition?

- Are there other details that I can add as additional body paragraphs to create a fuller or more complete paper?

- Are some of my sentences weak or confusing? Should they be removed because they do not relate to my thesis?

- Do my body paragraphs appear in the best possible order? Could I place them in a different order that is more logical or effective?

- Is each sentence constructed as well as it should be? *Read each sentence in each paragraph as if it were the only sentence on the page. This helps you to catch sentence fragments, run-on sentences, misspellings, and grammatical errors.*

- Does my ending paragraph obviously conclude my presentation? Does it reinforce my thesis statement? Is there a "clincher" sentence?

Practice Use the Evaluation Form on the page following this lesson to evaluate the research paper that you wrote for Lesson 16. Read your research paper carefully as you check for the items listed on the Evaluation Form. Write YES or NO in the blank next to each question.

When you are finished, you will either be confident that you have a strong research paper, or you will know where it needs to be improved.

If you answered NO to one or more of the questions on the Evaluation Form, rewrite to improve those areas.

When you can answer YES to every question on the Evaluation Form, you will have completed this assignment.

52

Research Paper Evaluation Form

Subject: _____

_____ Are my sources reliable, objective, and current?

_____ Is my introductory sentence interesting? *If it is not interesting to you, it certainly will not be interesting to the reader.*

_____ Does the beginning of the research paper clearly establish a formal, serious tone?

_____ Does the thesis clearly state the purpose of the paper?

_____ Does each body paragraph have a clear topic sentence at the beginning that tells the reader exactly what the paragraph will be about? *Read each topic sentence without the rest of the paragraph to see if it can stand alone as a strong idea.*

_____ Do the details all contribute to the reader's understanding of the thesis?

_____ Within each paragraph, are my sentences in a logical or practical order?

_____ Does each paragraph (except for the first paragraph) begin with an effective transition?

_____ Is each piece of borrowed material properly documented? Have I credited each of my sources?

_____ Are all of my sentences strong and clear? Do they all directly relate to the thesis?

_____ Do my body paragraphs appear in the best possible order? Is their order logical and effective?

_____ Is each sentence structured as well as it could be? *Read each sentence in each paragraph as if it were the only sentence on the page. This helps you identify fragments, run-on sentences, and the overall strength or weakness of each sentence.*

_____ Does my concluding paragraph summarize my research and reinforce my thesis statement? Is there a "clincher" sentence?

53

LESSON
18

Preparing to Write a
Personal Narrative

Personal Narrative

Narrative writing tells a story or relates a series of events. In a **personal narrative,** the writer tells a story about a significant personal experience or event.

In this lesson, you will prepare to write a personal narrative in which you will share your feelings about how an experience affected you or taught you something. Your first-person account might include action, suspense, dialogue, and vivid description.

Choosing a Personal Experience

To think of an experience for a personal narrative that you would like to share, consider the following:

- a wonderful (or disastrous) first time that you did something

- a memorable struggle or hardship that you experienced

- a "turning point" in your life

- an interesting, exciting, humorous, or moving event in your life

- an unusual or once-in-a-life-time experience, such as touring a distant country, meeting a famous person, or making an amazing discovery

Reading through the daily journals that you have written might give you additional ideas.

Brainstorming

On a piece of scratch paper, quickly write every experience that comes to your mind. When you have finished, select the one that you think is most interesting and write it on another piece of paper.

After selecting the experience you plan to write about in your personal narrative, begin brainstorming in order to recall details or emotions about this experience. List all words and phrases that come to mind. Without concern for spelling or grammar, write everything that occurs to you.

Organizing your Information Once you have gathered your thoughts and memories, begin to plan your narrative by organizing the events in a logical order, which might be chronological order—the sequence in which the events occurred. Your rough plan might look something like this:

First: My brother and I went hiking in Dark Canyon...

Then: We wandered off the main trail and...

Then: The sun went down and...

Then: We heard coyotes, wolves, and...

Finally: We learned how important it is to carry a compass and a flashlight.

Practice For your personal narrative, write a rough plan similar to the one above. In the next lesson, you will expand each part of this plan into a paragraph and complete your narrative by filling in detail, action, and dialogue.

55

LESSON 19

Writing a Personal Narrative

In Lesson 18, you chose an interesting personal experience and created a rough plan for writing a personal narrative. In this lesson, you will use your rough plan and any other notes and begin writing your narrative.

Opening Paragraph   Remember that your opening paragraph should capture the interest of the reader and establish your tone, which reveals your feelings or attitudes about the experience. You will write in first person, using the pronoun *I* or *we*.

Body Paragraphs   Although you have a plan to follow, you may alter it as you write. Following the opening paragraph, each "then" part of your rough plan might become the topic sentence for a body paragraph in which you fill in details, actions, and any necessary dialogue.

Concluding Paragraph   Your concluding paragraph will include a personal summary or commentary about how the experience affected you or taught you something significant.

Practice   Write your personal narrative according to the guidelines above. Include an opening paragraph, two or more body paragraphs, and a concluding paragraph.

56

LESSON 20

Evaluating the Personal Narrative

All of our writing is "work in progress." The knowledge that *writing is a process* guides our thinking throughout the construction of our personal narrative. From the first steps in selecting an experience to share, to organizing our thoughts, to creating body paragraphs, to adding transitions, we constantly make changes to improve our work.

Evaluating Your Writing

In Lesson 19, you completed your personal narrative. Now that some time has passed, you are ready to evaluate it using the following guidelines.

Ask yourself these questions:

- Is my introductory sentence interesting? *If it is not interesting to you, it certainly will not be interesting to the reader.*

- Does the beginning of the narrative clearly establish the tone?

- Does each body paragraph have a clear topic sentence at the beginning that tells the reader exactly what the paragraph will be about? *Read each topic sentence without the rest of the paragraph to see if it can stand alone as a strong idea.*

- Is the first-person point of view consistently maintained throughout the narrative?

- Are there other details, descriptions, emotions, or dialogue that I could add to make a more interesting narrative?

- Are my sentences in a logical or chronological order?

- Does each paragraph (except for the first) begin with an effective transition? Have I used a variety of time-related terms to sequence (order) the events?

- Are there other details that I can add as additional body paragraphs to create a fuller or more complete narrative?

- Are some of my sentences weak or confusing? Should they be removed because they do not relate to the story?

- Do my body paragraphs appear in the best possible order? Could I place them in a different order that is more logical or effective?

- Is each sentence constructed as well as it should be? *Read each sentence in each paragraph as if it were the only sentence on the page. This helps you to catch sentence fragments, run-on sentences, misspellings, and grammatical errors.*

- Does my concluding paragraph contain a summary or commentary about how the experience affected me? Is there a "clincher" sentence?

Practice Use the Evaluation Form on the page following this lesson to evaluate the personal narrative you wrote for Lesson 19. Read your narrative carefully as you check for the items listed on the Evaluation Form. Write YES or NO in the blank next to each question.

When you are finished, you will either be confident that you have a strong personal narrative, or you will know where it needs to be improved.

If you answered NO to one or more of the questions on the Evaluation Form, rewrite to improve those areas.

When you can answer YES to every question on the Evaluation Form, you will have completed this assignment.

58

Personal Narrative Evaluation Form

Title: _____

_____ Is my introductory sentence interesting? *If it is not interesting to you, it certainly won't be interesting to the reader.*

_____ Does the beginning of the narrative clearly establish the tone?

_____ Is the first-person point of view consistently maintained throughout the narrative?

_____ Does each body paragraph have a clear topic sentence at the beginning that tells the reader exactly what the paragraph will be about? *Read each topic sentence without the rest of the paragraph to see if it can stand alone as a strong idea.*

_____ Do the details all contribute to the reader's understanding of my personal experience?

_____ Within each paragraph, are my sentences in a logical or practical order?

_____ Does each paragraph (except for the first paragraph) begin with an effective transition?

_____ Are there no other details that I can add as additional body paragraphs to create a fuller or more complete narrative?

_____ Are all of my sentences strong and clear? Do they all directly relate to the story?

_____ Do my body paragraphs appear in the best possible order? Is their order logical and effective?

_____ Is each sentence structured as well as it could be? *Read each sentence in each paragraph as if it were the only sentence on the page. This helps you identify fragments, run-on sentences, and the overall strength or weakness of each sentence.*

_____ Does my concluding paragraph contain a personal summary or commentary about how the experience affected me or taught me something?

59

LESSON 21

Preparing to Write a Descriptive Essay

Descriptive writing describes a person, place, object, or event. With language that appeals to the senses, descriptive writing creates pictures in the reader's mind. Strong, vivid, and precise words are essential in creating clear descriptions.

In this lesson, we shall discuss the use of modifiers, comparisons, and sensory expressions to create accurate and complete descriptions. Then, you will prepare to write a descriptive essay about a person whom you can observe as you are writing.

Modifiers To add detail, we can use modifiers—adjectives and adverbs, phrases and clauses. Modifiers supply additional information, making nouns and verbs more specific and precise.

> *Fearless*, *flawless*, and *unflappable*, the super-hero stood *confidently* within arm's reach of the enemy.

Comparisons In addition to adding modifiers, we can use comparisons to make a description more vivid. *Simile* and *metaphor* are two kinds of comparisons. A *simile* expresses similarity between two things by using the word *like* or *as*:

> *Like* a pogo stick, the border collie hopped over clumps of daisies in the meadow.

A *metaphor*, on the other hand, describes one thing as though it were another thing:

> She was springy and energetic, a *pogo stick* with fur.

Both comparisons, simile and metaphor, help the reader to see a fuller picture of the border collie.

Sensory Expressions To create a more vivid image, we can appeal to the reader's five senses by detailing things that one can see, hear, smell, taste, and touch. For example, we can hear an engine *rumble*, see a snowflake *glisten*, smell the *perfume* of a rose, feel the *scratchiness* of a wool sweater, and taste the *tart* apple that makes our lips pucker.

60

Below, Washington Irving describes Ichabod Crane, the schoolmaster, in "The Legend of Sleepy Hollow."

> He was tall, but exceedingly lank, with narrow shoulders, long arms and legs, hands that dangled a mile out of his sleeves, feet that might have served for shovels, and his whole frame most loosely hung together. His head was small, and flat at top, with huge ears, large green glassy eyes, and a long snip nose, so that it looked like a weathercock perched upon his spindle neck, to tell which way the wind blew.

Irving's description demonstrates how a writer can use details, modifiers, and comparisons to give the reader a clear picture of an imaginary person.

In her novel *Johnny Tremain*, Esther Forbes uses metaphor and sensory images to describe a place. Notice how Boston is personified:

> Boston slowly opened its eyes, stretched, and woke. The sun struck in horizontally from the east, flashing upon weathervanes—brass cocks and arrows, here a glass-eyed Indian, there a copper grasshopper—and the bells in the steeples cling-clanged, telling the people it was time to be up and about.

In the same novel, the author goes on to describe Johnny Tremain:

> Johnny was already in his leather breeches, pulling on his coarse shirt, tucking in the tails. He was a rather skinny boy, neither large nor small for fourteen. He had a thin, sleep-flushed face, light eyes, a wry mouth, and fair, lank hair. Although two years younger than the swinish Dove, inches shorter, pounds lighter, he knew, and old Mr. Lapham knew, busy Mrs. Lapham and her four daughters and Dove and Dusty also knew, that Johnny Tremain was boss of the attic, and almost of the house.

The examples above show how good authors create vivid pictures using details, modifiers, comparisons, and sensory expressions.

Brainstorming After choosing one person whom you can observe as you write, you are ready to begin brainstorming in order to gather precise and concrete details that will appeal to the reader's senses and fully describe that person.

You might want to consider these aspects of the person:

1. Physical appearance—size, age, gender; colors, shapes, and textures of hair, eyes, skin, and clothing; peculiar features or facial expressions; movements and gestures;

2. Personality traits—mannerisms, habits, usual disposition. By their actions, people may demonstrate that they are intense or relaxed, hyperactive or laid-back, outgoing or shy, humble or proud, etc.

61

3. How the person affects others and the world around him or her: Where does the person live? What does the person do? What are his or her passions or interests? How does he or she relate to others? How does this person make you or other people feel?

On a blank piece of paper, quickly write everything that comes to your mind concerning the person you wish to describe. Without regard for spelling or grammar, write all the nouns, verbs, adjectives, adverbs, phrases, clauses, comparisons, and sensory expressions that occur to you.

Using Reference Materials Use reference materials such as dictionaries and thesauruses, both print and digital, to find additional precise and appropriate words and phrases for your essay.

Recognizing Connotations **Connotations** are the associations and emotions suggested by some words. A word's *denotation*, its literal, dictionary definition, is distinct from its *connotation*, which is its implied or suggested meaning. Words such as *floor, table* and *pencil* do not have connotations. However, such words as *flamboyant, condescending*, and *patronizing* do.

Consider the word pairs below. Which word from each pair has a more positive connotation?

profession, job   *acquaintance, friend*

stuff, belongings   *humility, inferiority*

We see that the words *profession, friend, belongings,* and *humility* have more positive connotations.

Consider the word pairs below. Which word from each pair has a more negative connotation?

stubborn, determined   *gaze, stare*

exult, boast   *child, urchin*

We see that the words *stubborn, stare, boast,* and *urchin* have more negative connotations.

We must learn to recognize word connotations to choose the best words to convey our meaning.

Organizing your Information Once you have gathered your thoughts and observations, begin to plan your descriptive essay by grouping the words and phrases into clusters. You might have one cluster of words and phrases that describe the person's physical

appearance; another cluster focusing on the person's personality; and another telling about what the person does, or how the person affects others and the world around him or her.

You can use each idea cluster to develop a topic sentence for each body paragraph in your essay.

Thesis Statement In your essay, you will be describing many different aspects of one person. What is the main impression that you want your reader to receive concerning this person? Your thesis statement will sum up that which is most important.

Practice For your descriptive essay, write a thesis statement and three or more topic sentences about the person you wish to describe. In the next lesson, you will develop each topic sentence into a body paragraph by adding more detail. Keep your brainstorming paper and this assignment in your three-ring binder so that you will be ready to complete your essay.

63

Writing a Descriptive Essay

LESSON
22

In Lesson 21, you prepared to write your descriptive essay about a person of your choice. By brainstorming, you gathered ideas and details. Then, you organized those details into clusters representing main ideas. From those clusters, you created a thesis statement and at least three topic sentences. Now, you are ready to write the complete essay.

Practice Using the topic sentences you wrote for Lesson 21, follow the steps below to complete the expository essay.

1. Develop each topic sentence into a body paragraph, keeping your thesis in mind. Refer to your brainstorming notes and idea clusters to write body sentences that add more detail and create a vivid picture in the reader's mind.

2. Create an introductory paragraph and a concluding paragraph. Remember that the introductory sentence should grab the reader's interest and that the "last words" of your conclusion will leave a lasting impression.

3. Add transitions between body paragraphs to make your ideas easier for the reader to follow. Pay special attention to the transition into the concluding paragraph.

4. Finally, put all the parts together to form a complete essay. As you are working, make any necessary corrections to your previous work. You might add things, take things out, or make any other change that results in a clearer, fuller descriptive essay.

Additional Practice (Optional) After you have evaluated your descriptive essay using the guidelines in Lesson 23, you might try writing another descriptive essay on a topic of your choice or on one of these topics:

1. A character from a novel you have read

2. A room in your house or apartment

3. A pet, or an animal that interests you

4. An interesting or beautiful outdoor scene

5. A sporting event, birthday party, or other kind of celebration

64

LESSON 23

Evaluating the Descriptive Essay

Because *writing is a process* and all of our writing is "work in progress," we constantly make changes to improve our work.

Evaluating Your Writing

In Lesson 22, you completed your descriptive essay. Now that some time has passed, you are ready to evaluate it using the following guidelines.

Ask yourself these questions:

- Is my introductory sentence interesting? *If it is not interesting to you, it certainly will not be interesting to the reader.*

- Does the thesis statement focus on a single person, place, object, or event?

- Does the thesis statement give my main impression of the person, place, object, or event that I am describing?

- Does each body paragraph have a clear topic sentence at the beginning that tells the reader exactly what the paragraph will be about? *Read each topic sentence without the rest of the paragraph to see if it can stand alone as a strong idea.*

- Are there other details, modifiers, comparisons, or sensory expressions I could add to help the reader to visualize my topic?

- Are my sentences in a logical order?

- Does each paragraph (except for the first) begin with an effective transition?

- Are there other details that I can add as additional body paragraphs to create a fuller or more complete description?

- Are some of my sentences weak or confusing? Should they be removed because they do not relate to the topic?

- Do my body paragraphs appear in the best possible order? Could I place them in a different order that is more logical or effective?

- Is each sentence constructed as well as it should be? *Read each sentence in each paragraph as if it were the only*

sentence on the page. This helps you to catch sentence fragments, run-on sentences, misspellings, and grammatical errors.

- Does my concluding paragraph sum up my main impression of the person, place, object, or event? Is there a "clincher" sentence?

Practice   Use the Evaluation Form on the page following this lesson to evaluate the descriptive essay you wrote for Lesson 22. Read your descriptive essay carefully as you check for the items listed on the Evaluation Form. Write YES or NO in the blank next to each question.

When you are finished, you will either be confident that you have a strong descriptive essay, or you will know where it needs to be improved.

If you answered NO to one or more of the questions on the Evaluation Form, rewrite to improve those areas.

When you can answer YES to every question on the Evaluation Form, you will have completed this assignment.

66

Descriptive Essay Evaluation Form

Topic: _____

_____ Is my introductory sentence interesting? *If it is not interesting to you, it certainly will not be interesting to the reader.*

_____ Does the thesis statement focus on a single person, place, object, or event?

_____ Does the thesis statement give my main impression of that person, place, object, or event?

_____ Does each body paragraph have a clear topic sentence at the beginning that tells the reader exactly what the paragraph will be about? *Read each topic sentence without the rest of the paragraph to see if it can stand alone as a strong idea.*

_____ Do the details all contribute to the reader's ability to visualize or mentally experience my topic?

_____ Within each paragraph, are my sentences in a logical order?

_____ Does each paragraph (except for the first paragraph) begin with an effective transition?

_____ Have I used enough modifiers, comparisons, and sensory expressions to enable the reader to visualize my topic?

_____ Are all of my sentences strong and clear? Do they all directly relate to the topic?

_____ Do my body paragraphs appear in the best possible order? Is their order logical and effective?

_____ Is each sentence structured as well as it could be? *Read each sentence in each paragraph as if it were the only sentence on the page. This helps you identify fragments, run-on sentences, and the overall strength or weakness of each sentence.*

_____ Does my concluding paragraph sum up my main impression of my topic?

67

LESSON 24

Preparing to Write an Imaginative Story

We have practiced writing vivid descriptions of people, places, objects, or events using details, modifiers, comparisons, and sensory expressions. We have also written a personal narrative with dialogue, logical sentence order, and effective transitions. In this lesson, we shall use all the writing skills that we have learned so far in order to create our own imaginative story.

An imaginative story is fiction; it is not a true story although it may be based on something that really happened.

Conflict, characters, setting, and plot are all parts of the imaginative story. In preparing to write our story, we shall gather information concerning each of these parts.

Conflict
A short story must have a problem or situation in which struggle occurs. A character may be in conflict with another character, with the forces of nature, with the rules of society, or even with his or her own self, as an internal conflict brought about by pangs of conscience or feelings of ambivalence.

For example, notice the possible conflicts related to the two situations below.

SITUATION 1: A drought hits a farming community.
Conflict: Some farmers steal water from others to keep their crops from dying.
Conflict: Local government officials try to enforce water rationing.

SITUATION 2: The substitute teacher has fallen asleep during the class's silent reading period.
Conflict: Some students want to take advantage of the situation and misbehave; others want to continue their silent reading.
Conflict: One student worries that the class will be punished for misbehavior.
Conflict: One student is embarrassed, for the sleeping substitute teacher is his aunt!

68

To find a situation and conflict for your own imaginative story, you might talk to friends or family members, watch the news, read the newspaper, or observe what is happening in the lives of people around you.

In preparation for story-writing, spend several minutes brainstorming with the help of a friend, teacher, or family member to gather ideas of situations and conflicts. Write down all the situations and possible resulting conflicts that come to mind. Then, choose the one conflict that most interests you for your imaginative story.

Tone   Your attitude toward the conflict will create the **tone** of your story. The details and language that you use might evoke joy, fear, amusement, grief, or some other emotion. For example, you will want your story to make the reader laugh if you feel that the situation facing the characters is funny. On the other hand, if you feel that the situation is serious and worrisome, you will try to increase the reader's anxiety.

After choosing your conflict, plan how you will establish the tone of your story by answering the following questions:

1. What is my attitude toward the conflict and the characters involved in it?

2. What details can I use to create this mood, or evoke these emotions, in the reader?

Point of View   You may tell your story from either the first-person or third-person point of view.

In the first-person point of view, the story is narrated, using the pronoun *I*, by one person who either participates in or witnesses the conflict. Only the narrator's thoughts are expressed, as in the example below.

> *Rapping my knuckles on her desk, I demanded her reply. But she just sat there like a bump.*

In the third-person, or omniscient, point of view, the story is narrated by someone outside the story, someone who knows everything: each character's thoughts and actions. This allows the writer to reveal what any character thinks or does, as in the example below.

69

Rapping her knuckles on Christie's desk, Mary demanded to know where Christie had hidden the chocolate. But having no intention of giving away her secret, Christie stubbornly ignored the inquiry.

Before you begin writing your imaginative story, you must choose an appropriate point of view from which to tell about the conflict.

Characters To create a captivating story, you must develop interesting and believable characters. Engaged in a struggle, the main character, or *protagonist*, might be opposed by another character, an *antagonist*. There may be other characters as well.

As you develop your characters, attempt to keep them consistent in their behavior and show logical reasons for any change in their behavior. For example, if an ordinarily greedy character suddenly acts generous, you must explain why.

Invent your characters by noting their physical appearance, actions, and personality traits.

Dialogue Dialogue is the spoken words of characters. A character's words can reveal things about the character's personality, background, thoughts, and attitudes. You can use dialogue to develop your characters and make your story more interesting.

Spend a few minutes brainstorming in order to gather ideas about your main characters. Give each one a name, some physical attributes, and a distinctive personality.

Setting The setting is the time and place of the action. Vivid, specific details help to describe the setting of a story. You must consider both location and time. Does your story take place indoors, in a specific room; or outdoors, on a mountain, beach, or prairie? Or, does it take place on an airplane, boat, or train? Do the events occur in the morning, afternoon, or evening? Does the story happen in the past, present, or future?

Decide where and when your story will take place and jot down a few details that you can use later to describe your setting.

70

Plot The plot is the action of your story. Once you have chosen a conflict, one or more characters, and the setting of your story, you are ready to develop the action using this story plan:

BEGINNING OF STORY

Present your characters.

Establish the setting and tone.

Introduce the conflict.

MIDDLE OF STORY

List a series of actions that build to a climax.

END OF STORY

Resolve the conflict, or show why it cannot be resolved.

Use the plan above to make notes, which you can expand later into a full imaginative story.

Practice Follow the instructions in this lesson for brainstorming, choosing a conflict, deciding on the tone and point of view, inventing characters, describing the setting, and planning the plot of your imaginative story. On a separate piece of paper, answer the following questions:

1. Who are your characters? Give a brief description of each.

2. What is the setting? Give the time and place.

3. Describe the tone, the emotions the reader will experience.

4. What is the conflict?

5. Briefly list some actions that will build to a climax.

6. How will you resolve the conflict?

Keep your answers to these questions in your three-ring binder. In the next lesson, you will use this information as you write your imaginative story.

71

Writing an Imaginative Story

LESSON 25

In Lesson 24, you prepared to write your imaginative story. By brainstorming, you gathered ideas and details. You chose a conflict, decided on the tone and point of view, invented characters, described your setting, and roughly planned the plot. Now, you are ready to write the imaginative story.

Keep this plan in front of you as you write:

BEGINNING OF STORY

Present your characters.

Establish the setting and tone.

Introduce the conflict.

MIDDLE OF STORY

List a series of actions that build to a climax.

END OF STORY

Resolve the conflict, or show why it cannot be resolved.

Practice Using your notes from Lesson 24 and the plan above, follow the steps below to write your story.

1. Write an introductory sentence that will grab the reader's attention.

2. At the beginning of the story, in whatever order you think is best, establish the setting and tone, present your characters, and introduce the conflict.

3. Add dialogue in order to reveal more about your characters' personalities, thoughts, and motivations.

4. Keep the point of view consistent throughout the story.

5. Write a series of actions that build to a climax.

6. Resolve the conflict at the end of your story, or show why it cannot be resolved.

72

Evaluating the Imaginative Story

LESSON 26

Because *writing is a process,* and all of our writing is "work in progress," we constantly make changes to improve our work.

Evaluating Your Writing

In Lesson 25, you completed your imaginative story. Now that some time has passed, you are ready to evaluate it using the following guidelines.

Ask yourself these questions:

- Does my introductory sentence capture the reader's attention?

- Does the beginning of the story establish the tone and suggest the conflict?

- Are the characters believable and interesting?

- Have I revealed the characters' personalities and motivations through dialogue and action as well as description?

- Are my characters consistent in their behavior? Have I adequately explained any changes from their normal behavior?

- Are there other details, modifiers, comparisons, or sensory expressions I could add to help the reader to visualize the setting?

- Do the actions flow logically from one to another?

- Do the actions build suspense?

- Does the dialogue sound natural?

- Does the point of view remain constant throughout the story?

- Are some of my sentences weak or confusing? Should any be removed because they do not relate to the story?

- Do my sentences appear in the best possible order? Could I place them in a different order that is more logical or effective?

- Is each sentence constructed as well as it should be? *Read each sentence in each paragraph as if it were the only sentence on the page. This helps you to catch sentence fragments, run-on sentences, misspellings, and grammatical errors.*

- Is the end of the story believable and satisfying? Has the conflict been resolved?

Practice   Use the Evaluation Form on the page following this lesson to evaluate the imaginative story that you wrote for Lesson 25. Read your story carefully as you check for the items listed on the Evaluation Form. Write YES or NO in the blank next to each question.

When you are finished, you will either be confident that you have a strong imaginative story, or you will know where it needs to be improved.

If you answered NO to one or more of the questions on the Evaluation Form, rewrite to improve those areas.

When you can answer YES to every question on the Evaluation Form, you will have completed this assignment.

74

Imaginative Story Evaluation Form

Title: _____

_____ Does my introductory sentence capture the reader's attention?

_____ Does the beginning of the story establish the tone and suggest the conflict?

_____ Are the characters believable and interesting?

_____ Have I revealed the characters' personalities and motivations through dialogue and action as well as description?

_____ Are my characters consistent in their behavior? Have I adequately explained any change from their normal behavior?

_____ Have I included sufficient details, modifiers, comparisons, and sensory expressions to enable the reader to visualize the setting?

_____ Do the actions flow logically from one to another?

_____ Do the actions build suspense?

_____ Does the dialogue sound natural?

_____ Does the point of view remain consistent throughout the story?

_____ Is each sentence strong and clear? Does each sentence relate to the story?

_____ Is each sentence structured as well as it could be? *Read each sentence in each paragraph as if it were the only sentence on the page. This helps you identify fragments, run-on sentences, and the overall strength or weakness of each sentence.*

_____ Is the end of the story believable and satisfying? Has the conflict been resolved?

75

LESSON 27

Writing a Chapter Summary

A summary is a relatively brief restatement of the main ideas in something one has read. In a summary, the writer omits details and condenses a long passage—a whole story, chapter, or book—to its main ideas. Therefore, the summary is much shorter than the original passage.

In this lesson, we shall practice writing a one-paragraph summary of a chapter in a novel.

Chapter Summary If you were reading a novel to a friend, and if your friend fell asleep during one of the chapters, he or she might miss a great deal of the action or story line. Your brief *summary* of that missing chapter could help your friend to continue quickly to the next chapter without confusion and without rereading the entire chapter.

Example Below is a summary of *The Phantom Tollbooth*, Chapter 1. Notice the present tense of verbs.

> In this chapter we meet Milo, the main character, who is one day very bored, so he goes to his room. In his room, Milo finds a package, and inside is a tollbooth. The tollbooth comes with tokens to get Milo from place to place. The places are strange places that Milo has never heard of before. Milo decides to go to Dictionopolis, which is very far away. When we finish this chapter, Milo is on his way to Dictionopolis.
>
> Summary by Lilah Arenas

Practice In a single paragraph, summarize one chapter of a novel you are reading or have read in the past (or a novel from the list below). Your paragraph should not exceed 150 words. Your summary should include major characters and provide a sense of what happens in the chapter. Use present tense.

Suggested novels for this exercise:

The Wizard of Oz, by Frank L. Baum

The Secret Garden, by Frances Hodgson Burnett

A Tale of Two Cities, by Charles Dickens

The Jungle Book, by Rudyard Kipling

A Wrinkle in Time, by Madeleine L'Engle

The Lion, the Witch, and the Wardrobe, by C.S. Lewis

76

Writing a Short Story Summary

We have learned that a summary condenses a longer passage to a shorter one, leaving out details and giving only the main ideas of the original passage.

In this lesson, we shall practice writing a one-paragraph summary of a short story.

Short Story Summary
If you had read an interesting short story and wanted to tell a friend about it, you might give your friend a *summary* of the story. You would not tell the *whole* story or give away the ending. Instead, you would summarize, giving some general information about the main characters, setting, and major conflict.

Example
Below is a summary of the short story "Rikki-tikki-tavi," by Rudyard Kipling. Notice the present tense of verbs.

> Rikki-tikki, a baby mongoose, gets washed away in a flood and ends up lying in the hot sun in the middle of a garden path, looking like he's dead. A little boy named Teddy finds Rikki-tikki and tells his parents. Teddy's father rescues the little mongoose, and the family decides to keep him as a pet. An evil cobra named Nag and his equally evil wife, Nagaina, are afraid because mongooses kill snakes, so they try to kill Teddy and his family, hoping that Rikki-tikki will then go away also. Overhearing Nag and Nagaina's plan to kill Teddy and his family, Rikki-tikki makes his own heroic plan to kill the cobras.

Summary by Abby Grace Remington

Practice
Write a one-paragraph summary of the imaginative story that you wrote for Lesson 25. Your paragraph should not exceed 150 words. Your summary should include general information about main characters, setting, and plot. Use present tense.

Additional Practice
Read one of the short stories suggested below or one that your teacher suggests. Then, put the book away and write a one-paragraph summary of the story, using present tense. Your paragraph should not exceed 150 words. Your summary should include general information about main characters, setting, and plot.

Suggested reading:

"The Great Stone Face," by Nathaniel Hawthorne

"Old Times on the Mississippi," by Mark Twain

"Old Yeller," by Fred Gipson

"The Christmas Carol," by Charles Dickens

"The Human Comedy," by William Saroyan

"On Borrowed Time," by Paul Osborn

LESSON 29

Preparing to Write Poetry

Writing poetry allows us to tap into our imagination, experience, and our knowledge of descriptive writing. To write a poem, we must focus our full attention on our subject in order to express impressions, emotions, and images related to it.

As we write poetry, we can communicate our feelings through rhythms and repeated sounds as well as through the words we choose. In this lesson, we shall discuss traditional poetry, free verse, simple steps for selecting a subject, and methods for gathering thoughts in preparation for writing a poem.

Traditional Poetry The following poem is an example of **traditional poetry,** the type of poetry established long ago, which has a regular rhythmic, rhyming pattern.

> We search the world for truth; we cull
> The good, the pure, the beautiful,
> From graven stone and written scroll,
> And all old flower-fields of the soul;
> And, weary seekers of the best,
> We come back laden from the quest,
> To find that all the sages said
> Is in the Book our mothers read.
>
> JOHN GREENLEAF WHITTIER (1807–1892)

Free Verse In contrast to traditional poetry, **free verse** does not have a regular rhyme or rhythm pattern and is frequently used by writers today. The following poem, titled "Silence," is an example of free verse.

> My father used to say,
> "Superior people never make long visits,
> have to be shown Longfellow's grave
> or the glass flowers at Harvard.
> Self-reliant like the cat—
> that takes its prey to privacy,
> the mouse's limp tail hanging like a shoelace
>   from its mouth—
> they sometimes enjoy solitude,

and can be robbed of speech
by speech which has delighted them.
The deepest feeling always shows itself in silence;
not in silence, but restraint."
Nor was he insincere in saying, "Make my
    house your inn."
Inns are not residences.

MARIANNE MOORE (1887–1972)

Although the free verse above does not contain rhyme or regular rhythm, it is full of clear, sharp images. Notice the simile, "Self-reliant like the cat...".

Selecting a Subject In selecting a subject for a poem, make a list of things about which you feel strongly. Using the lines provided, write your ideas for each of the following:

• an important person in your life

_____

• a place you remember with strong emotion

_____

• an activity that you love or hate

_____

•your most or least favorite season or time of day

_____

• your most or least favorite holiday

_____

• a meaningful experience or observation

_____

• a possession that you value

_____

• music that you enjoy or dislike

_____

• your most or least favorite animal

_____

• your most or least favorite food

_____

• an object that you appreciate or despise

_____

After writing one or more ideas under each category above, think about why you feel strongly about each item. Then, circle three that you would consider using as the subject of a poem.

Gathering Thoughts about your Subject

Using a separate sheet of paper, brainstorm about at least one of your three possible subjects circled above, as in the following example:

Grandma's house

fresh-baked cookies and pies   rose garden
aroma of coffee   Grandpa playing the saxophone
exploring the attic   Uncle Rob on the banjo
old toys and bicycles   a photo album
fun with cousins   the cuckoo clock
hide-and-seek
laughter and singing
the candy dish
tire swing
picking cherries

After brainstorming, place a check mark beside the ideas that most clearly express your feelings. Copy those onto another sheet of paper leaving plenty of space between each one for more details. Then, write as many specific details as you can

to fully describe each expression, as in the following example:

√ A photo album
　　dust that tickles my nose
　　yellowed with age, fragile pages that crinkle as I turn them
　　black and white photographs of prim and proper ancestors whom
　　　　I never knew, peculiar-looking people from the old country, such as
　　Great Aunt Lottie with stern expression, thin lips that make a straight
　　　　line, piercing eyes, tight-fitting dark gown with many buttons
　　　　and white ruffles at the neck

Practice　Complete the steps given in this lesson for selecting a subject and gathering thoughts for your own poem. Save your notes in your three-ring binder so that you can add to them at any time. You will use these notes for writing poems in the next two lessons.

82

LESSON
30

Writing a Traditional Poem

We have learned that a traditional poem has regular rhythm and rhyme. In this lesson, we shall discuss a few different ways to create rhythm and rhyme in a traditional poem.

Rhythm   Rhythm is the regular repetition or orderly recurrence of sounds or accented syllables. To create rhythm, we combine words to take advantage of their natural accents. Notice the alternating stressed and unstressed syllables in the following lines:

A gi/ant li/zard held/ my hand
And star/ted dan/cing with/ the band

ANONYMOUS

Tell me/ not, in/ mournful/ numbers,
Life is/ but an/ empty/ dream.

HENRY WADSWORTH LONGFELLOW

Although most traditional poetry has a regular rhythmic pattern, this pattern may not be the same in every line. It may change from one line to another, remaining consistent within the whole poem, as in the example below. Notice that the first and third lines each have five accents; however, the second and fourth lines each have only three accents.

Brave/ men/ who work/ while o/thers sleep
Who dare/ while o/thers fly—
They/ build/ a na/tions pi/llars deep
And lift/ them to/ the sky.

RALPH WALDO EMERSON

Rhyme   In addition to rhythmic patterns, we can create rhyming patterns to enhance our poetry. Patterns of repeated sounds may be regular or random. They may occur at the beginning, middle, or end of lines. Traditional poetry contains regular rhyme as well as regular rhythm. In Ralph Waldo Emerson's poem above, the last word in every other line of the stanza (a grouping of lines in a poem) rhymes. However, James

83

Whitcomb Riley's poem below is written in couplets, two successive rhyming lines that form a unit:

Away

I cannot say and I will not say
That he is dead—he is just away!
With a cheery smile and a wave of the hand
He has wandered into an unknown land.
And left us dreaming how very fair
It needs must be since he lingers there
And you—O you, who the wildest yearn
For the old-time step and the glad return,
Think of him faring on, as dear
In the love of There as the love of Here.

Another common rhyming pattern is the limerick, which is often used in humorous poetry. It follows an AABBA rhyme scheme, meaning that each limerick is made up of two couplets plus a fifth line that rhymes with the first two, as in the example below:

[A] There once was a miser named Clarence
[A] Who Simonized both of his parents;
[B] "The initial expense,"
[B] he remarked, "is immense,
[A] But it saves on the wearance and tearance."

OGDEN NASH

Practice Using some of the ideas that you developed in the previous lesson, write a traditional poem of at least four lines with regular rhyme and rhythm. Try to rhyme important words with words that support the meaning of your poem. Be mindful of stressed and unstressed syllables as you create a rhythm with your words.

84

LESSON 31

Writing a Free-verse Poem

We have learned that free verse does not have regular rhyme or rhythm. In free verse, repeated sounds are more likely to be irregular and inexact, like the sounds of speech. Sensory details and vivid language create clear images and strong messages. In this lesson, we shall use all that we have learned about descriptive writing and poetry to create our own free-verse poem.

Repeated Sounds
In free verse, repeated sounds may occur at the beginning, middle, or end of lines. They may be in the form of *assonance*, the repetition of a particular vowel sound; *consonance*, the repetition of a particular consonant sound within or at the end of words; or *alliteration,* the repetition of identical or similar sounds at the beginning of words.

ASSONANCE: nine fine rhymes entwined

CONSONANCE: Pale Dolly, sallow and ill

ALLITERATION: baseball batter with bulging biceps

In addition to the types of repeated sounds above, free verse may employ rhyming words, but they are not confined to a certain pattern as in traditional poetry. For example, a line of free verse might include these words: ache/fake/snake/lake

Figurative Language
In writing free verse, poets also use figurative language, or *figures of speech*, which include the simile, the metaphor, and the personification. We have learned to create vivid descriptions using sensory detail and comparisons, such as similes and metaphors. We remember that the simile expresses similarity between two things by using the word *like* or *as*:

The ungodly are...*like* the chaff which the wind drives away.   PSALM 1:4, NEW KING JAMES VERSION

All we *like* sheep have gone astray.

ISAIAH 53:6, NEW KING JAMES VERSION

For He shall grow up before Him *as* a tender plant, And *as* a root out of dry ground.

ISAIAH 53:2, NEW KING JAMES VERSION

85

The metaphor, on the other hand, describes one thing as though it were another thing:

> We are His people and the sheep of His pasture.
>
> PSALM 100:8, NEW KING JAMES VERSION

> His truth shall be your shield and buckler.
>
> PSALM 91:4, NEW KING JAMES VERSION

Another form of figurative language is *personification*, a metaphor in which human qualities are given to nonliving things, abstract ideas, or animals. Notice how the moon is personified in the following metaphor:

> The moon smiled down on the children and winked…

Simile, metaphor, and personification will enhance your free verse.

Practice   Using the ideas that you developed in Lesson 29, or some new ideas, write a free-verse poem of at least eight lines. Concentrate on important words that express your ideas, and put them in a meaningful order. Try to create clear, vivid images using sensory details: sights, sounds, smells, and other physical sensations. In addition, you might use simile, metaphor, or personification as well as repeated sounds.

86

LESSON 32   Writing in Response to Literature

We read many books and magazines for pleasure; however, there are times when we are expected to analyze and reflect on what we read. This is called active reading. In active reading, you ask yourself what kind of text you are reading. Is it fictional? an essay? an editorial? Then, you decide on the author's purpose. Is it to entertain, inform, or persuade? Next, you pinpoint the main idea, or find the thesis. Finally, you find evidence in the text to support your thoughts about the main idea or thesis.

When we write about literature, we use the present tense of verbs as in the sentence below.

Tom Sawyer *discovers* a great law of action.

In this lesson, we shall read an excerpt from *The Adventures of Tom Sawyer* and practice writing in response to it. We shall draw evidence from the text to support our analysis and reflection as we answer questions.

Carefully read the following excerpt from Chapter 2: "The Glorious Whitewasher." *The Adventures of Tom Sawyer.* Twain, Mark. New York: Modern Library, 2001. (1876)

But Tom's energy did not last. He began to think of the fun he had planned for this day, and his sorrows multiplied. Soon the free boys would come tripping along on all sorts of delicious expeditions, and they would make a world of fun of him for having to work—the very thought of it burnt him like fire. He got out his worldly wealth and examined it—bits of toys, marbles, and trash; enough to buy an exchange of *work*, maybe, but not half enough to buy so much as half an hour of pure freedom. So he returned his straightened means to his pocket, and gave up the idea of trying to buy the boys. At this dark and hopeless moment an inspiration burst upon him! Nothing less than a great, magnificent inspiration.

He took up his brush and went tranquilly to work. Ben Rogers hove in sight presently—the very boy, of all boys, whose ridicule he had been dreading. Ben's gait was the hop-skip-and-jump—proof enough that his heart was light and his anticipations high. He was eating an apple, and giving a long, melodious whoop, at intervals, followed by a deep-toned ding-dong-dong, ding-dong-dong, for he was personating a steamboat. As he drew near, he slackened speed, took the middle of the street, leaned far over to starboard and rounded to ponderously and with laborious pomp and circumstance,

for he was personating the "Big Missouri," and considered himself to be drawing nine feet of water. He was boat and captain and engine-bells combined, so he had to imagine himself standing on his own hurricane-deck giving the orders and executing them:

"Stop her, sir! Ting-a-ling-ling!" The headway ran almost out, and he drew up slowly toward the sidewalk.

"Ship to back! Ting-a-ling-ling!" His arms straightened and stiffened down his sides.

"Set her back on the stabboard! Ting-a-ling-ling! Chow! ch-chow-wow! Chow!" His right hand, meantime, describing stately circles—for it was representing a forty-foot wheel.

"Let her go back on the labboard! Ting-a-ling-ling! Chow-ch-chow-chow!" The left hand began to describe circles.

"Stop the stabboard. Ting-a-ling-ling! Stop the labboard! Come ahead on the stabboard! Stop her! Let your outside turn over slow! Ting-a-ling! Chow-ow-ow! Get out that head-line! *Lively* now! Come—out with your spring-line—what're you about there! Take a turn round that stump with the bight of it! Stand by that stage, now—let her go! Done with the engines, sir! Ting-a-ling-ling! *Sh't! s'h't!sh't!*" (trying the gauge-cocks.)

Tom went on whitewashing—paid no attention to the steamboat. Ben stared a moment and then said, "Hi-*yi*! *You're* up a stump, ain't you!"

No answer. Tom surveyed his last touch with the eye of an artist, then he gave his brush another gentle sweep and surveyed the result, as before. Ben ranged up alongside of him. Tom's mouth watered for the apple, but he stuck to his work. Ben said:

"Hello, old chap, you got to work, hey?"

Tom wheeled suddenly and said:

"Why, it's you, Ben! I warn't noticing."

"Say—I'm going in a swimming, I am. Don't you wish you could? But of course you'd druther *work*—wouldn't you? Course you would!"

Tom contemplated the boy a bit, and said:

"What do you call work?"

"Why, ain't *that* work?"

Tom resumed his whitewashing, and answered carelessly:

"Well, maybe it is, and maybe it ain't. All I know, is, it suits Tom Sawyer."

"Oh come, now, you don't mean to let on that you *like* it?"

The brush continued to move.

"Like it? Well, I don't see why I oughtn't to like it. Does a boy get a chance to whitewash a fence every day?"

That put the thing in a new light. Ben stopped nibbling his apple. Tom swept his brush daintily back and forth—stepped back to note the effect—added a touch here or

there—criticized the effect again—Ben watching every move and getting more and more interested, more and more absorbed. Presently he said:

"Say, Tom, let *me* whitewash a little."

Tom considered, was about to consent, but he altered his mind:

"No—no—I reckon it wouldn't hardly do, Ben. You see, Aunt Polly's awful particular about the fence—right here on the street, you know—but if it was the back fence I wouldn't mind and *she* wouldn't. Yes, she's awful particular about this fence; it's got to be done very careful; I reckon there ain't one boy in a thousand, maybe two thousand, that can do it the way it's got to be done."

"No—is that so? Oh come, now—lemme just try. Only just a little—I'd let *you*, if you was me, Tom."

"Ben, I'd like to, honest injun; but Aunt Polly—well, Jim wanted to do it, but she wouldn't let him; Sid wanted to do it, and she wouldn't let Sid. Now don't you see how I'm fixed? If you was to tackle this fence and anything was to happen to it—"

"Oh, shucks, I'll be just as careful. Now lemme try. Say—I'll give you the core of my apple."

"Well, here—. No, Ben, now don't. I'm afeard—"

"I'll give you *all* of it!"

Tom gave up the brush with reluctance in his face, but alacrity in his heart. And while the late Steamer "Big Missouri" worked and sweated in the sun, the retired artist sat on a barrel in the shade close by, dangled his legs, munched his apple, and planned the slaughter of more innocents. There was no lack of material; boys happened along every little while; they came to jeer, but remained to whitewash. By the time Ben was fagged out, Tom had traded the next chance to Billy Fisher for a kite, in good repair; and when *he* played out, Johnny Miller bought in for a dead rat and string to swing it with—and so on, and so on, hour after hour. And when the middle of the afternoon came, from being a poor poverty-stricken boy in the morning, Tom was literally rolling in wealth. He had beside the things before mentioned, twelve marbles, part of a jews-harp, a piece of blue bottle-glass to look through, a spool cannon, a key that wouldn't unlock anything, a fragment of chalk, a glass stopper of a decanter, a tin soldier, a couple of tadpoles, six fire-crackers, a kitten with only one eye, a brass doorknob, a dog-collar—but no dog—the handle of a knife, four pieces of orange-peel, and a dilapidated old window-sash.

He had a nice, good, idle time all the while—plenty of company—and the fence had three coast of whitewash on it! If he hadn't run out of whitewash he would have bankrupted every boy in the village.

Tom said to himself that it was not such a hollow world, alter all. He had discovered a great law of human action, without knowing it—namely, that in order to make a man or a boy covet a thing, it is only necessary to make the thing

difficult to attain. If he had been a great and wise philosopher, like the writer of this book, he would have now comprehended that Work consists of whatever a body is *obliged* to do, and that Play consists of whatever a body is not obliged to do. And this would help him to understand why constructing artificial flowers or performing on a tread-mill is work, while rolling ten-pins or climbing Mont Blanc is only amusement. There are wealthy gentlemen in England who drive four-horse passenger-coaches twenty or thirty miles on a daily line, in the summer, because the privilege costs them considerable money; but if they were offered wages for the service, that would turn it into work and then they would resign.

The boy mused a while over the substantial change which had taken place in his worldly circumstances, and then wended toward headquarters to report.

Practice Using present tense, answer the following questions about the excerpt above. Draw evidence from the excerpt to support your analysis and reflection. You may work independently, with your teacher, or with other classmates.

1. Give specific examples of the author's sense of humor.

2. What piece of wisdom does Mark Twain offer the reader?

3. What is the "great law of human action"?

4. How does the reader know the minds of little boys?

5. How can one describe Tom? Give specific examples.

6. Cite a figure of speech from this passage and explain its meaning.

7. Mark Twain wrote in the late 1800s. Based on what you read in this passage, compare and contrast boys in the 1800s to boys now.

After answering the questions above, compare your answers with the examples at the end of this Writing Packet.

90

LESSON 33

Writing in Response to Informational Text

We often read to learn something more about a subject or to learn something new. There are times when we are asked to analyze and reflect on what we read.

In this lesson, we shall practice active reading as we examine a part of an informational article about geology. Carefully read the excerpt below.

"Geology." U*X*L *Encyclopedia of Science.* Edited by Rob Nagel. Farmington Hills, Mich: Gale Cengage Learning, 2007. (2007)

> Geology is the scientific study of Earth. Geologists study the planet—its formation, its internal structure, its materials, its chemical and physical processes, and its history. Mountains, valleys, plains, sea floors, minerals, rocks, fossils, and the processes that create and destroy each of these are all the domain of the geologist. Geology is divided into two broad categories of study: physical geology and historical geology.
>
> Physical geology is concerned with the processes occurring on or below the surface of the Earth and the materials on which they operate. These processes include volcanic eruptions, landslides, earthquakes, and floods. Materials include rocks, air, seawater, soils, and sediment. Physical geology further divides into more specific branches, each of which deals with its own part of Earth's materials, landforms, and processes. Mineralogy and petrology investigate the composition and origin of minerals and rocks. Volcanologists study lava, rocks, and gases on live, dormant, and extinct volcanoes. Seismologists use instruments to monitor and predict earthquakes and volcanic eruptions.
>
> Historical geology is concerned with the chronology of events, both physical and biological, that have taken place in Earth's history. Paleontologists study fossils (remains of ancient life) for evidence of the evolution of life on Earth. Fossils not only relate evolution, but also speak of the environments in which the organisms lived. Corals in rocks at the top of the Grand Canyon in Arizona, for example, show a shallow sea flooded the area around 290 million years ago. In addition, by determining the ages and types of rocks around the world, geologists piece together continental and oceanic history over the past few billion years. Plate tectonics (the study of the movement of the sections of Earth's crust) adds to Earth's story with details of the changing configuration of the continents and oceans.

91

Practice After carefully reading the excerpt above, answer the following questions, drawing evidence from the excerpt to support your answers. You may work independently or with your teacher or other students. Use present tense of verbs.

1. What is geology?

2. Define the difference between physical and historical geology.

3. Are seismologists and volcanologists physical or historical geologists? What do they study?

4. What branch of historical geology studies fossils?

5. Why would plate tectonics be useful?

After answering the questions above, compare your answers with the "Example Answers" at the end of this Writing Packet.

92

LESSON 34

Sentence Conciseness

Conciseness is the expression of much in few words. Effective writing is concise and clear; it is not cluttered with unnecessary words. In this lesson, we will learn to avoid superfluous words and to reduce wordy clauses and phrases.

Avoiding Superfluous Words

Superfluous words are needless. They do not add to the meaning of the sentence. We can avoid wordiness by eliminating superfluous words and the unnecessary repetition of ideas. Notice the difference between the first and second sentences in the following pairs.

WORDY: Fluffy has six baby kittens.

CONCISE: Fluffy has six kittens.

     (*Baby kittens* is redundant, or needlessly repetitive.)

WORDY: Fluffy's collar is red in color.

CONCISE: Fluffy's collar is red.

     (The words *in color* are unnecessary because red is a color.)

WORDY: We have a weekly spelling test every Friday.

CONCISE: We have a weekly spelling test.

              or

          We have a spelling test every Friday.

     (*Weekly* and *every Friday* are redundant.)

WORDY: I did well on the test owing to the fact that I had studied.

CONCISE: I did well on the test because I had studied.

     (The phrase *owing to the fact that* is wordy.)

WORDY: The list is entirely complete.

CONCISE: The list is complete.

     (The word *complete* cannot be modified. A thing is either complete, or it isn't.)

Other examples of wordiness include the expressions *very unique* and *slightly impossible.* The words *unique* and *impossible,* like the word *complete,* cannot be modified.

Example 1   Rewrite the following sentences making them more concise.

(a) My train leaves at eight a.m. in the morning.

(b) The big giant fell with a thump.

(c) The noise was barely audible to my ears.

(d) We planted some tiny miniature roses.

(e) In my opinion, I think skydiving is scary.

Solution   (a) **My train leaves at eight a.m.** (or) **My train leaves in the morning.** The expressions *a.m.* and *in the morning* are redundant.

(b) **The giant fell with a thump.** The word *big* is unnecessary.

(c) **The noise was barely audible.** *To my ears* is unnecessary since *audible* refers only to the sense of hearing and not to seeing, smelling, tasting, or touching.

(d) **We planted some miniature roses.** (or) **We planted some tiny roses.** *Tiny* and *miniature* are redundant.

(e) **In my opinion, skydiving is scary.** (or) **I think skydiving is scary.** *In my opinion* and *I think* are redundant.

Reducing Wordy Clauses and Phrases   Sometimes we can make our sentences more concise by reducing clauses to phrases, or phrases to single words. Notice how clauses are reduced to phrases or appositives in the sentence pairs below.

CLAUSE: *When I was stuck in traffic,* I listened to the radio.

PARTICIPIAL PHRASE: *Stuck in traffic,* I listened to the radio.

CLAUSE: They decided *that they would take the train.*

INFINITIVE PHRASE: They decided *to take the train.*

CLAUSE: *When the sun rises,* the birds begin to sing.

PREPOSITIONAL PHRASE: *At sunrise,* the birds begin to sing.

CLAUSE: Mr. Chen, *who is the department head,* wrote the test.

APPOSITIVE: Mr. Chen, *the department head,* wrote the test.

94

Example 2 Revise the following sentences by reducing the italicized clauses to phrases or appositives.

(a) We will wait for a sale *so that we can save money.*

(b) I am learning a piano piece *that was composed by Mozart.*

(c) I invited Miss Lopez, *who is my English teacher,* to join us.

Solution (a) **To save money, we will wait for a sale.** We reduce the adverb clause to an infinitive phrase.

(b) **I am learning a piano piece *composed by Mozart*.** We reduce the adjective clause to a participial phrase.

(c) **I invited Miss Lopez, *my English teacher*, to join us.** We reduce the adjective clause to an appositive.

Notice how clauses and phrases are reduced to single words in the sentences below.

CLAUSE: We will prune the branches *that have been broken.*

WORD: We will prune the *broken* branches.

PHRASE: His career *in the field of photography* was challenging.

WORD: His *photography* career was challenging.

PHRASE: Let us write *in a concise manner.*

WORD: Let us write *concisely.*

Example 3 Revise the following sentences by reducing the italicized clauses or phrases to single words.

(a) I saw a spider *that was enormous.*

(b) Do you enjoy the music *of Mozart*?

(c) Sally sings *in a harmonious way.*

Solution (a) **I saw an *enormous* spider.**

(b) **Do you enjoy *Mozart's* music?**

(c) **Sally sings *harmoniously*.**

95

Practice Rewrite sentences 1–4, making them more concise.

1. Combine together the sugar, flour, and spices.

_____

2. Should we vote to re-elect him again for President?

_____

3. We shall study anthropology for a period of a month.

_____

4. Your writing style is very unique.

_____

Revise sentences 5 and 6 by reducing the italicized clauses to phrases of appositives.

5. The rancher *who had come from Iowa* had never seen the ocean.

_____

6. The monument, *which is situated in Colorado*, marks the continental divide.

_____

Revise sentences 7 and 8 by reducing the italicized phrases or clauses to single words.

7. We have been reading poetry *that was written by Longfellow.*

_____

8. Hepzy listened *in an attentive manner.*

_____

When you have completed Practice exercises 1—8 above, compare your answers with the example answers in the Appendix of this Writing Packet.

96

LESSON 35

Dictionary Information about a Word

Definitions A dictionary's main function is to provide word meanings. Because a single word may have many meanings, we carefully read all its definitions.

Parts of Speech Usually, an italicized abbreviation indicates the part of speech of the word being defined. A dictionary's front or back matter explains its abbreviations, like the ones below.

n.	noun	*v.*	verb
adj.	adjective	*adv.*	adverb
pron.	pronoun	*prep.*	preposition
conj.	conjunction	*interj.*	interjection
vt.	transitive verb	*vi.*	intransitive verb

Spelling The boldfaced word that begins a dictionary entry gives the accepted spelling. If there are two or more accepted spellings, these are given as well. The dictionary also provides the spelling of irregular plurals, principal parts of verbs, comparative or superlative forms of adjectives, and other grammatical changes in word forms.

Syllable Division We have learned to divide a word between its syllables when the word must be divided at the end of a line. The boldfaced dictionary entry shows syllable division by a dot or by a space.

con·gress   con gress

Pronunciation Using a fixed symbol for each of the common English sounds, the pronunciation guide respells the entry word with accent marks to show which syllables are spoken with more stress than the others. A heavier mark indicates the heaviest accent, or stress on the syllable; a lighter mark indicates a lighter accent.

tech·ni·cal·ity   tek´ ni kal´ ə tē

Etymologies **Etymologies** are word histories showing the word's original language and meaning. Usually, the dictionary's front matter explains abbreviations used to indicate the languages from

which words come. The symbol < or the abbreviation *fr.* may mean "from." See examples below.

DICTIONARY ABBREVIATION	MEANING
< F	from French
< Heb-Aram	from Hebrew-Aramaic
fr. OE	from Old English
< Gr	from Classical Greek
< Heb	from Hebrew
fr. L	from Latin

Field Labels Some dictionary words are not part of our general vocabulary but have to do with a special subject, area, or usage. These words may have **field labels** such as the ones below.

SUBJECT LABELS

Med. (medicine)	*Chem.* (chemistry)
Zool. (zoology)	*Music*
Baseball	*Comput.* (Computer Science)

AREA LABELS

Netherl. (Netherlandic)	*Scotland*
Northwest U.S.	*NGmc* (North Germanic)

USAGE LABELS

Dialect	*Slang*	*Rare*
Informal	*Old-fashioned*	*Literary*
Archaic	*Obsolete*	*Vulgar*

Synonyms and Antonyms At the end of an entry, a dictionary may list **synonyms** (SYN, words of similar meaning) and/or **antonyms** (ANT, words of opposite meaning).

Practice Use a dictionary to complete the following.

1. Write two different definitions for the word *disregard.*

_____

_____

98

2. Write the part of speech indicated by the dictionary for the word *eucalyptus*.

_____

3. Write two accepted spellings for the plural of *eucalyptus*.

_____

4. Rewrite the word *opportunistic* showing its syllable division.

_____

5. Rewrite the word *opaque* showing its pronunciation, including accent marks.

_____

6. The word *resuscitate* comes from what language?

_____

7. Write the field label given to the word *pianissimo*.

_____

8. Write a synonym for the word *facile*.

_____

Review Lesson

<u>When Misty came home from school, she discovered that her cat, Scamp, was missing</u>. First she walked up and down the street, calling his name. Then she searched through the garage, the backyard, and the front yard. Just as she was ready to give up the search, Misty found Scamp sleeping peacefully behind the sofa in the living room.

During math and social studies, Dudley draws cute little elves in his notebook with a pencil. Sometimes science lectures inspire him to draw exotic plants and animals. His notebook is full of intricate and interesting sketches. <u>Dudley is an outstanding doodler</u>!

<u>I've never seen a bird as peculiar as the heron</u>. A wading bird found in temperate and tropical regions, the heron has long thin legs with knobby knees. Its neck is so long and slender that I wonder how it can swallow anything. Its pointed bill and unusual head feathers give the heron an appearance unlike any other bird I've seen.

Lillian has read hundreds of stories about the wild West, and she can recite them all word for word. <u>Lillian dreams of becoming a cowgirl someday</u>. You'll never see her wearing anything but Western attire—jeans with chaps, boots, and a bandana. Although she doesn't own a horse, she is saving her money to buy one.

Lesson 1

1. The ability to communicate clearly and effectively in writing connects us with people and enhances our prospects for future success in school and in the workplace.

2. We need to become skillful writers.

3. In the first place, writing well allows us to communicate with other people.

4. In the first place...

5. In conclusion...

Lesson 13

I. Grammatical terms
  A. Parts of speech
    1. Noun
    2. Pronoun
    3. Verb
    4. Adverb
    5. Adjective
    6. Preposition
    7. Interjection
    8. Conjunction
  B. Parts of a sentence
    1. Subject
    2. Predicate
    3. Direct object
    4. Indirect object

  C. Punctuation marks
    1. Period
    2. Comma
    3. Semicolon
    4. Colon
    5. Dash
    6. Question mark
    7. Quotation marks
    8. Exclamation mark

(Subtopics may be in any order.)

100

Example Answers for Lesson 32

1. The author demonstrates a sense of humor in a number of ways. One example is when Mark Twain describes Ben's "personating a steamboat." It is very amusing. Another example is Mark Twain's choice of valuable, boys' trinkets. Still another example is when Mark Twain calls himself a wise, old philosopher, "like the writer of this book."

2. Mark Twain's main piece of wisdom is this: "Work consists of whatever a body is *obliged* to do, and Play consists of whatever a body is not obliged to do."

3. Tom Sawyer discovers "a great law of action—without knowing it—namely, that in order to make a man or a boy covet a thing, it is only necessary to make the thing difficult to attain."

4. Mark Twain demonstrates understanding of little boys in a number of ways. First, Tom's worldly wealth is described a "bits of toys, marbles, and trash."

   Second, boys do not want to miss a desirable experience. So Tom's manipulation of his friends is believable. Tom paints his chore of whitewashing a fence as fun, and the boys decide that maybe Tom is right. Tom's friends do the whitewashing for him.

   Also, Tom's payments from the boys shows how well Mark Twain understands the workings of their minds. Here are the author's words: "Tom was literally rolling in wealth. He had besides the things before mentioned, twelve marbles, part of a jews-harp, a piece of blue bottle-glass to look through, a spool cannon, a key that wouldn't unlock anything, a fragment of chalk, a glass stopper of a decanter, a tin soldier, a couple of tadpoles, six fire-crackers, a kitten with only one eye, a brass doorknob, a dog-collar—but no dog—the handle of a knife, four pieces of orange peel, and a dilapidated old window sash."

5. Tom is the typical boy. He does not enjoy doing his chores—in this case, whitewashing the fence. Also, he is manipulative. He tricks his friends into painting the fence for him. In addition, he is intelligent. He sells his chore and gathers more boyish treasures than he had when he began his work.

101

6. The author uses simile, "the very thought of it *burnt him like fire,"* to convey Tom's emotional pain when others make fun of him.

7. Boys in the 1800s do not have televisions, computers, cell phones, or electronic games. Their toys are simple—marbles, kites, tadpoles, and so forth. However, boys in the 1800s have the same basic feelings and desires as boys today. They all want to have fun, to use their imaginations as Ben does when imitating a steamboat, and to be accepted by their peers as Tom does when pretending that whitewashing a fence is a prestigious job.

Example Answers for Lesson 33

1. Geology is the study of the Earth.

2. Physical geology examines activities on or below the surface of the earth, while historical geology examines the physical and biological events in the Earth's history.

3. Seismologists and volcanologists are physical geologists. They study different activities of the earth. Seismologists track and predict earthquakes. They also study the activity of volcanoes (eruptions). Volcanologists focus on the lava, rocks, and gases produced by active, inactive, or extinct volcanoes.

4. Fossils are studied by paleontologists.

5. Plate tectonics studies the movement of the Earth's crust. It helps scientists understand why volcanoes erupt, how earthquakes occur, and where faults (breaks in the Earth's surface) are located.

Example Answers for Lesson 34

1. Combine the sugar, flour, and spices.

2. Should we vote to re-elect him for President?

3. We shall study anthropology for a month.

4. Your writing style is unique.

5. The rancher from Iowa had never seen the ocean.

6. The monument in Colorado marks the continental divide.

7. We have been reading Longfellow's poetry.

102

8. Hepzy listened attentively.

Answers for Lesson 35

1. Answers will vary. 1. to pay no attention to. 2. a lack of attention.

2. noun

3. eucalyptuses, eucalypti

4. op·por·tun·is·tic

5. ō pak´

6. Latin

7. *Music*

8. smooth, flowing, fluent (answers will vary).